THE TIN STREAMS OF WENDRON

JUSTIN BROOKE

TWELVEHEADS PRESS

TRURO • 1994

CONTENTS

Many of the sites of bounds, tin-streams, stamps and mines mentioned in this work are on private land, and permission should be sought from the owner before exploring them. Much of the district is boggy or heavily overgrown, and is unsafe. Few shafts or adits are recorded on modern maps. Those who intend to explore should go in pairs or parties, preferably in the company of someone who knows the ground well.

Front cover illustration: **Dressing plant, 1920s, Porkellis Moor.** *Eric Edmonds*

TWELVEHEADS PRESS

First published 1994 by Twelveheads Press,
Chy Mengleth, Twelveheads, Truro, Cornwall TR4 8SN.

ISBN 0 906294 32 0
British Library Cataloguing-in-Publication Data.
A catalogue record for this book is available from the British Library.

Printed by The Amadeus Press Ltd., Huddersfield, Yorks.

FOREWORD

TIN-STREAMING, THE WASHING of alluvial deposits to recover tin oxide, is undoubtedly one of Cornwall's oldest industries. Yet surprisingly it has attracted little attention, apart from the authoritative paper by William Jory Henwood, FGS, which appeared over a century ago. The recent discovery of a hitherto unpublished manuscript provided the stimulus for the present work, which originally took the form of a paper read to the Cornish Institute of Engineers. It deals with tin-streaming and its associated activities in an area at one time second only to St Austell in importance, and brings together many of the historical, financial, legal, technical and human aspects of the industry.

The relatively simple nature of tin-streaming and the almost universal illiteracy among the early streamers militated against the keeping of records apart from leases and receipts of dues, and it has thus not been possible to produce figures by which the outputs, costs and recoveries can be judged. Such records as have survived are in Imperial measures and £sd, and I make no apology for using them, since to convert them to other units would be misleading.

I record my gratitude to the numerous people who have helped me in the research for this work, notably the staffs of the County Record Office and of the Royal Institution of Cornwall in Truro. For permission to quote from published works my thanks are due to the University Presses of Oxford and Cambridge, to George Allen & Unwin Ltd, to the Camborne School of Mines, and to the executors of the late Dr A. K. Hamilton Jenkin. I am particularly grateful to Professor Robert R. Pennington, Ll.D., of the Faculty of Commercial Law at the University of Birmingham and to my friend and Cornish-language Bard, Hugh Miners, *Den Toll*, for reading the typescript and for offering many useful suggestions. To the generations of patient and persevering tin-streamers of Wendron I also offer my thanks, with a special message of gratitude to the friendly and hospitable people of that parish, who have given me so much useful information and encouragement, and innumerable cups of tea.

Marazion, 1994
Justin Brooke

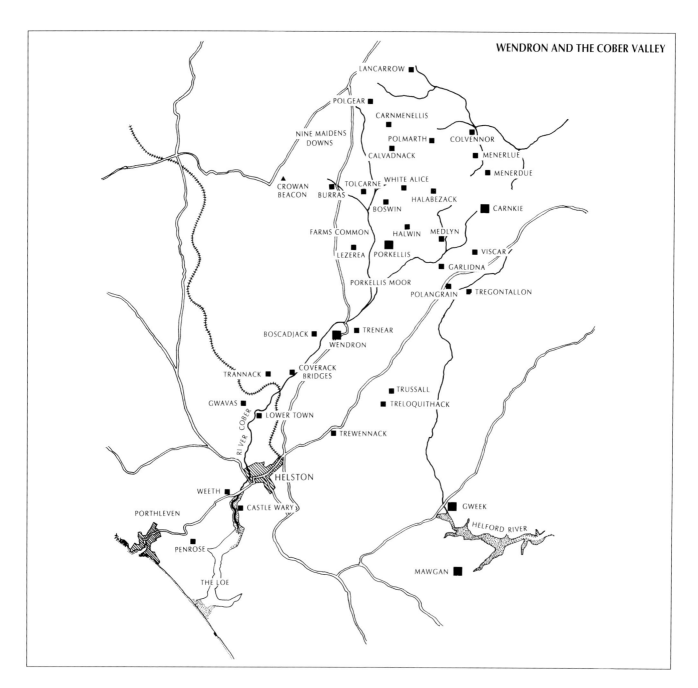

LANCARROW

POLGEAR

CARNMENELLIS

NINE MAIDENS
DOWNS

POLMARTH   COLVENNOR

CALVADNACK   MENERLUE

CROWAN
BEACON   TOLCARNE   WHITE ALICE   MENERDUE
BURRAS   HALABEZACK

BOSWIN   CARNKIE

FARMS COMMON   HALWIN   MEDLYN

LEZEREA   PORKELLIS   VISCAR

GARLIDNA

PORKELLIS MOOR
POLANGRAIN   TREGONTALLON

BOSCADJACK   TRENEAR
WENDRON

TRANNACK   COVERACK
BRIDGES
TRUSSALL
GWAVAS   TRELOQUITHACK

LOWER TOWN

TREWENNACK

HELSTON

WEETH

PORTHLEVEN   CASTLE WARY
GWEEK

PENROSE   HELFORD RIVER

THE LOE   MAWGAN

RIVER COBER

CHAPTER ONE
INTRODUCTION

WRITING IN THE fifteen-eighties, Norden observed of tin: 'It is a mettall growing for the moste parte amonge the hard and infragable rockes, in the Moares and mountayns, the owre thereof beyng an obdurate stone spred in the veynes of the mountaynes, where the workes and maner of working is of two sortes, Streame workes and Loade workes. The Stream workes are in the brookes, in valleys among the hills: The Loade workes in the mountaynes. The Streame workes are shallowe and more easie: The Loade workes deepe, paynfull and daungerous.'[1] Carew, who wrote at about the same time as Norden, added that stream-works included 'moore workes', which were similar to stream-works but lacked water, though they 'grew from the like occasion.'[2]

Forming an important part of the Stannary of Penwith and Kerrier, the area covered in this book is roughly eight miles from north to south and some six miles from east to west. It comprises the whole of the parish of Wendron, and parts of Helston, Sithney, Crowan, Stithians and Constantine, lying on the banks of streams which were worked on both sides and which formed parts of the parish boundaries. It lies on the central and southern part of the Carnmenellis granite and in a strip of metamorphosed killas along its southern margin. Now thinly populated, it contains extensive tracts of uncultivated moorland and croft. Traces of ancient tin-workings are still apparent in the valleys, despite the successful reclamation for agricultural purposes of several worked-over areas. The tin lodes, which are mainly in the granite, course roughly northeast, with a northerly underlie, and are numerous and narrow. Worked on their backs at surface by 'old men', they were often found when opened up by shafts to be too poor to be worked economically and to become barren at shallow depths. They represent the bottom part of the tin zone,[3] from whose upper parts the tin ore was washed down into the valleys to form the deposits whose workings are the subject of this study.

During the period of erosion of the rocks containing the tin-lodes the tin-gravels were formed. Of a greater specific gravity than the granitic gravel or growan formed from the rocks which had enclosed them, they were either scattered singly on the hillsides, when they were called shode, or accumulated in masses on the granite or killas bedrock in the bottoms of the valleys, forming layers of varying lengths and thicknesses known as streams of tin. When such a stream contained a good quantity of tin it was called a *bew heyle*, the Cornish for a live stream. When the gravels in the stream only contained a little tin the stream was said to be just alive, and when the stream contained no tin at all it was said to be dead. These streams of tin were of different widths, but seldom less than six feet wide, and were often scattered in varying quantities over the whole width of the moor, bottom or valley in which they were found. When several such streams met they often made a very rich floor of tin, as if one stream attracted another.[4] Generally, the detrital tin in Wendron was less rounded or less water-worn than that in other parts of Cornwall.[5]

As time went on a layer of sand and gravel settled on top of the tin-gravels, and this in turn was covered by layers of peat or vegetable mould. In the valley above Porkellis Bridge, for instance, sometimes as much as twelve feet of overburden lay on top of a layer of tin-gravels of the same thickness. At Carn Wartha, which lies on a tributary of the river Cober a short distance north of Tolcarne Mill,[6] the overburden consisted of angular and sub-angular masses of granite and of thin quartz and tourmaline vein stuff mixed with lumps of peat and quantities of granitic gravel and sand, the refuse of previous operations. The tin-ground consisted of quartzose, felspathic and tourmaline sand and gravel, unevenly sprinkled with more or less rounded granules of tin ore, of much the same character as those in the overlying rubbish. This part of the deposit, when worked for the first time, was also about twelve feet thick. The bedrock on which it rested, known as the shelf, was of disintegrated granite containing numerous small isolated bodies and short narrow veins of quartz and tourmaline, irregularly impregnated with tin ore.

Downstream from Carn Wartha, on the river Cober at Lezerea, the peat overburden was about four feet thick and contained hazel nuts and branches in its lower parts. This lay on two to three feet of coarse growan mixed with a little felspathic clay about two feet thick. Below this was the tin-ground, which was about three feet thick and composed of angular and somewhat rounded masses of tourmaline granite, largely mixed with tin-gravel. The bedrock was a decomposed felspathic granite, which was found to be tolerably uniform to a considerable depth, and to contain numerous small stringers or veins of tinny quartz rock. At Mean Vrose, on Porkellis Moor, south of the bridge and west of the village, great quantities of tin-gravel were obtained by the streamers who, on reaching the bedrock, discovered the outcrops of lodes which they worked to some depth.[7] In some places, such as the lower parts of Porkellis Moor, the overburden contained an upper and poorer layer of tin-ground, resting on a false shelf. On breaking through the false shelf a more ancient alluvium was found, resting on the bedrock, and generally rich in tin-gravel.[8] Occasionally there was more than one false shelf; and the tin-gravels lying on them were generally less rounded than those on the shelf.[9]

Tin-streaming, the oldest form of winning tin, was the name given to the means adopted to work the tin-gravels. It preceded underground mining for tin by several centuries, and its great antiquity is shown by the numerous Celtic Cornish terms and stream-names once used by the streamers, which are listed in Appendix A. As early as the eighteenth century the term was also applied to the working of tin-bearing wastes or slimes from stamping-mills which dressed ores from underground mines,[10] a meaning it retains to this day. It also included the working-over of ground previously streamed, the mode of working being almost the same, and it now covers the working of dumps from abandoned mines. In 1550 it was noted that tin-streaming was of greater importance in terms of output than underground or deep mining, but in 1778 it was said to be 'very simple and less important than deep Mining to the community in general', which suggests that by then the position had been reversed.[11] Meanwhile, in 1730 Tonkin noted that the old stream-works were said to have been 'in a manner exhausted', and that little moor tin or old stream tin (that is, tin from alluvial deposits being worked for the first time) was being raised.[12] Nevertheless, tin gravels and previously-streamed areas continued to be worked on a declining scale in Wendron up to the end of the eighteen-eighties and, intermittently, to the late 1920s.

Although it seems unlikely that deep mining for tin began

Porkellis Moor, Wendron. *Justin Brooke*

Porkellis Moor from the south, showing ancient tin workings and stream diversions. Garlidna Farm is in the right foreground. *Cornwall Archaeological Unit*

in Wendron much before the sixteenth century, it is probable that shallow openworks on the backs of lodes were made a century or two earlier, and possibly even before this. Seventy years ago experts believed that tin-working had gone on in Cornwall for certainly three thousand years,[13] but a recent writer shows that this may be too optimistic a figure, and notes that the winning of tin was not conducted continuously through the ages.[14] At times it came to a standstill for economic reasons; one of the periodical slumps in the

industry came in the sixteenth century, when 'the Tynne-workes began to fayle' and attention was turned to agriculture.[15]

Within the last century Cornwall has seen the virtual exhaustion of its stream-tin deposits, and for almost a hundred years the majority of streamers have confined their activities to the working and re-working of wastes from dressing-plants and dumps of deep mines. This, too, has seen a decline in recent years, due largely to the closure of many mines and to the employment on the remaining ones of better methods of recovering the very fine or slime tin, which had formerly passed out with the waste, as well as to economic

Lower Porkellis: the remains of Basset and Grylls installations in the distance *Justin Brooke*

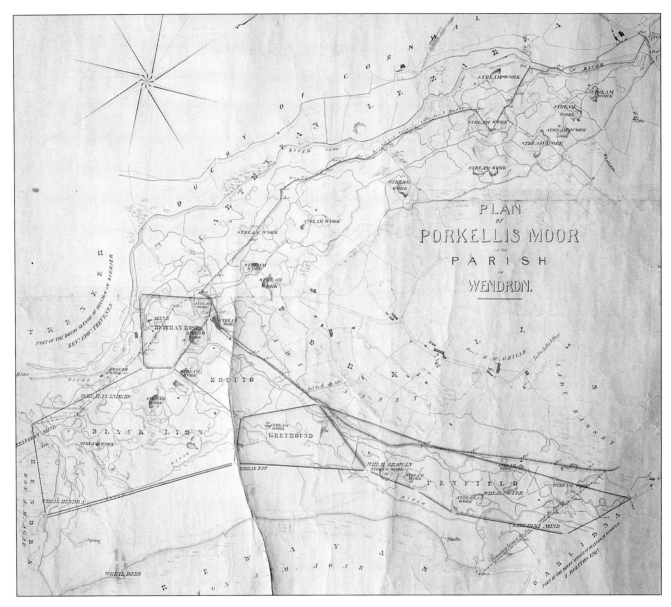

Map of Porkellis Moor, Wendron, c1836. *County Record Office, Truro.*

factors militating against small-scale workings. The tin-streams below Geevor mine at Pendeen and below South Crofty mine at Pool, for instance, were closed in the late 1960s owing largely to the installation of modern Mozley frames at the former and a new slimes plant at the latter.

In the first half of the last century it appears that Wendron, as a tin-streaming area, was second only in importance to St Austell, whose output of stream-tin in the eighteen-forties was larger than that of the whole of the rest of the county.[16] However, although Wendron did not have the large-scale workings of the kind found further east, and consequently attracted less attention, it played an important role from the legal point of view, and was the starting point for several lawsuits, one of which, as we shall see, turned out to be a leading case.

The main streaming areas lay in the valley of the river Cober, which rises below Dowha (from *dowr*, the Cornish for water) and runs southwards. Passing through Lezerea and Porkellis Moors, it flows past Wendron Forge at Trenear and through Helston to the Loe Pool, from whence it flows by a tunnel into the sea. On its way it is joined by tributaries, which have also been streamed, rising near Nine Maidens Downs, Crowan Beacon, Farms Common, Calvadnack and Carnkie, themselves fed by other small streams and springs. Below Porkellis Bridge the valley opens out into the wide and still largely uncultivated and unenclosed wilderness of Porkellis Moor. Here, among the patches of bracken, gorse, heather and sallow, can be seen traces of the workings of tin-streamers through the centuries, in the shape of water-filled openworks, heaps of waste sand and soil, level spaces where machinery may once have stood or which were banked round and used as slimes ponds, and diversions of the river from its original bed to feed water-wheels and streaming-plants. Here also are the concrete foundations and walls erected during the working of the Basset and Grylls mine. The largest water-filled excavations are near the southern boundary of the moor, between Lower Porkellis and Trenear, and, now much overgrown, provide a natural habitat for many varieties of flora and fauna.[17]

Other parts of Wendron that have been streamed for tin include the streams rising near Butteris and Treloar, on the eastern side of the parish which, with others rising near Trenethick, Trewennack and Trillian, run into the Helford river at Gweek. The Treloar stream contained the tin-streams of Retanna, Polangrain, Treloar and Crowgey. Another stream rises near the northern extremity of the parish between Lancarrow and Polgear, and runs eastwards down Kennal Vale to join an arm of the river Fal near the Norway Inn at Perran ar Worthal. In its upper stretches and tributaries this valley includes the tin-streaming moors of Lancarrow, Polgear, Polhigey, Menheryon, Colvenner (or Skidner), Menadue, Menerlue and Yellow Work, where much of the parts not covered by the waters of the Stithians reservoir have been reclaimed for agriculture. The deposits in these moors have been worked from ancient times, and it is generally agreed that Porkellis and Medlyn moors, the latter on a tributary of the Carnkie branch, have probably been turned over by tin-streamers a number of times.

That the works are ancient is shown by Norden, who noted in the fifteen-eighties that the 'chief tynn mynes' in Kerrier hundred were Roseline, Gorlimoe and Port Kellis, in Gwendern parish.[18] The first of these is recognisable four centuries later as Roselidden, which lay just north of Trenethick Wood Mine and which may have begun as a stream-work which developed into a shallow open-work on the back of a lode. In 1536 John Haymor, a freeman and lessee of Roslyn, was fined 44s. for raising tin and permitting others to raise it from his land. Furthermore, he was ordered to fill in the workings and not to work the tin without a licence.[19] Gorlimoe, subsequently Cardelucow alias Garledyna (1754), Coledna (1815), and now (1993) Garlidna, was both mined and streamed. A large area of shallow open-

The remains of old workings on Garlidna Moor, with Tyackes's engine house of Basset and Grylls mine in the distance. *Justin Brooke*

workings up to twenty feet deep on lodes coursing a little east of north can still be seen east of Garlidna farm on the hillside sloping northwards towards the moor, the latter now known as Ruby Bal and taking its name from a working just south of the stream. The workings were carried down as far as water permitted, and the ore thus raised would have been stamped at one of the many stamps driven by water diverted from the stream, whose two main branches rose at Carnkie and Halabezack. How long the open-works continued to be worked is not known, though a tin-stream on Garlidna moor,

in Duchy land, was worked by Edward Bolitho from 1841 to 1845, and possibly longer.[20] Port Kellis, a corruption of *Porth Kylly* (grove gate, recorded in 1498), is thought to have been the name given to the stream-works in the moor south and west of the village now known as Porkellis.

The importance of water to streaming operations, both for dressing and as a source of power, is self-evident, as noted by many early writers. In its course to the sea the river Cober and its tributaries were frequently turned out of their original courses and diverted along leats and launders to drive water-wheels, not only for pumping mines and stamping tin-ore but also for grinding corn. In the eighteenth and early nineteenth centuries water-wheels were described as water-engines or

Old tin works partly covered by nature, Polhigey Moor, Wendron. *Justin Brooke*

Water filled open works beside the road, Lower Porkellis. To the right one of the stacks erected for the Basset and Grylls mine. *Justin Brooke*

just as engines, while steam-engines were called fire-engines. An example of a large diversion of the river on Porkellis Moor is given in an agreement made in 1768, when Mr Basset of Tehidy granted permission, as far as his interest was concerned, to William Pasmore of Helston and his partners in the Great Adit on the Moor. From its description the work seems to have been a leat rather than a tunnel. The permission, for which an annual fee of two guineas was charged, enabled the adventurers in the Great Adit to convey water from Mr Glynn's Little Stamps in Porkellis (whose location has been lost) to Wheal Growan engine, in the leats then being used. A branch leat was used to carry part of the water from the Little Stamps direct to the new engine being built at Wheal an Dees, to which the residue of the Wheal Growan engine water was to pass by a leat then being cut. Wheal Growan later became part of Basset and Grylls mine, and Wheal an Dees, later Bal Dees, formed part of Wendron Consols mine in the nineteenth century. The two mines were some seven hundred yards apart, so that it appears that the arrangements made would have involved at least half a mile of diversions. For this William Pasmore and his partners would have been able to charge a rent;[21] at about the same time they laid out £5 on repairing the Ball Reeth adit, which may have been one of the sources of water for the Great Adit, and which subsequently became the Basset and Grylls adit.

It was not until nearly three centuries after Norden wrote that a description was given of Porkellis Moor, appropriately enough by George Henwood, a Cornish mining engineer. In 1858 he noted that it lay in a pan of ground, on nearly a dead level, and was surrounded by hills. It was not surprising that the accumulations of water in it were excessive and required powerful engines for drainage. Worked by streamers from time immemorial, it was celebrated for the quantity of tin ore it had afforded, which was said to amount to millions (of £s) in value. The moor abounded with vestiges of ancient and extensive operations, in the shape of old burrows and pits,

and extended for miles. Tradition gave a report of a small village near Helston having been the port where the Phœnicians traded with their small vessels for the much-prized mineral. Modern workers had found numerous old granite millstones and mortar-stones for pounding and grinding the ores, all bearing the marks of long and severe use. Small parcels of ore left by the old men were occasionally found, as were traces of ancient smelting-works or 'Jews' houses'. There were also numerous tin lodes which had been worked down as far as the water permitted. The moor was full of 'tinners' hutches' or large excavations full of water, which were dangerous and a great inconvenience to the regular miner. The ground was of a loose character, being growan or decomposed granite, and a part of the moor was known as the great clay.[22]

The tributary of the river Cober that rises near Carnkie and joins the main stream below Porkellis was regarded by a writer in 1875 as the main stream. He noted that at one stream-work near Fiscar a deep pit had been sunk from whence the mineral was obtained, and that as the ground was excessively wet a pump driven by a water-wheel was used to keep the pit dry. Recent explorations in some of the old men's workings lower down the valley 'show how carefully they searched for the treasure, digging to a great depth and fencing the sides of the pits with huge trunks of oak trees.'[23]

A more scientific approach was made in 1884 by Robert Hunt, F.R.S., the Keeper of the Mining Records, though his account was based on observations made some years earlier. The valley had by that time been streamed right from the source of the stream, where the alluvium, although shallow and comparatively poor, had all been turned over at some remote period. The underlying rock, which extended to a depth of twenty fathoms before becoming hard and glassy, was a coarse-grained semi-decomposed granite, traversed by heavy dark blue veins or 'capel' containing patches of tin ore. Near these veins the rock was often iron-stained. The tin-bearing veins became smaller and poorer in depth, and were not thought to be worth working. The tin-ore was sparsely diffused in the soil and gravel on the hillsides, which also appeared to have been turned over extensively. Towards the village of Porkellis the valley widened into an irregular basin, whose bottom had been very productive of stream-tin. The bedrock occurred at depths varying between six or seven to twenty fathoms (*sic*, for feet). In some places a false shelf was met with. Numerous veins of tin traversed the bedrock, all of them more or less productive. Below Porkellis, where the tributary joined the Cober, the valley widened out considerably, and it was probably here that it had been most productive of tin. The whole bed had repeatedly been turned over, and operations on some parts were still continued. With great labour a cutting had been brought down on one side,

from about a mile up the valley, by which means a number of small water-wheels had been put in motion to drain the workings. The Moor had a most desolate aspect. It was absolutely treeless, and was studded with irregular banks of gravel and patches of weeds, between which were deep black pools, the relics of abandoned works. Recently some of the banks had been levelled and covered with topsoil to convert the land into meadows,[24] an early instance of the land reclamation recommended by Pryce nearly a century earlier.[25]

Below Trenear the valley closes in and continues narrow and steep-sided for a couple of miles, to open out again below Lowertown. Just above the latter hamlet the contact between the Carnmenellis granite and the killas occurs, and from below this point to Helston town mills the bottom of the valley was very carefully streamed. but it fell into a decline

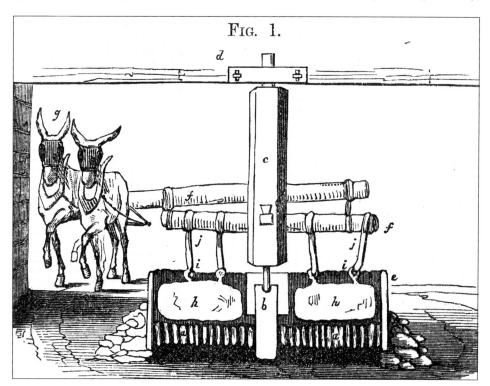

FIG. 1.

Chilian arrastre

towards the end of the eighteen-thirties, when it was barely profitable.[26] The alluvium here was mixed with large granite boulders, patches of which occurred on the killas. When the boulders were too large to be turned over the tin-gravel underneath was scraped out with a long-handled instrument. Small adits were driven into the base of the hillside formed by the detritus of the killas, to extract the underlying tin-gravel, and by 1840 there was little alluvial soil left in its original position. Many of the greenstone and porphyry (elvan) boulders here had one or more hemispherical cavities, showing that they had been used for mortars in which to pulverise tinstone. Other fragments of granite, probably of a later date, formed parts of rude crushing-mills similar to Chilean arrastres. Just above the surface junction of the granite and killas the valley is crossed by a hard bar of rock, running nearly east and west, which was quarried. In opening the quarries a few feet above the level of the river, several circular cavities were found, five inches to a foot and a half in diameter and from four to seven feet deep. These were formed by water which, over the centuries, had been eddying into fissures in the rock, and, carrying gravel round and round, had ground out the hollows, which contained pebbles of almost pure cassiterite.[27]

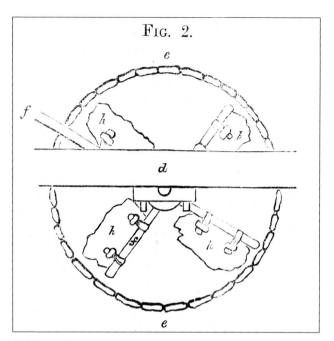

Chilian arrastre

ROSLYN (ROSELIDDEN) MINE

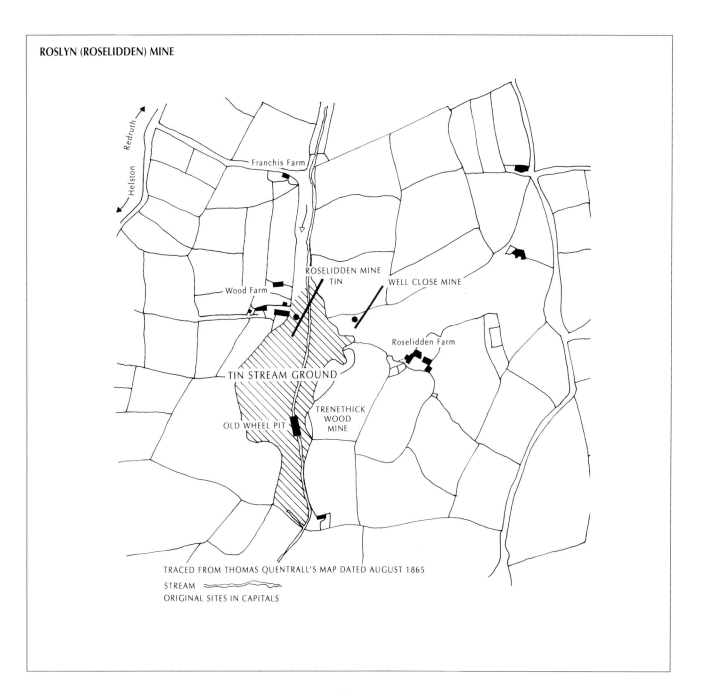

Redruth

Helston

Franchis Farm

ROSELIDDEN MINE
TIN

WELL CLOSE MINE

Wood Farm

Roselidden Farm

TIN STREAM GROUND

TRENETHICK
WOOD
MINE

OLD WHEEL PIT

TRACED FROM THOMAS QUENTRALL'S MAP DATED AUGUST 1865

STREAM

ORIGINAL SITES IN CAPITALS

CHAPTER TWO
STREAMING

ALTHOUGH CAREW AND Borlase refer to tin-streaming in 1602 and 1758 respectively, the most detailed early account was given in 1788, in *Mineralogia Cornubiensis*, which appeared ten years before the death of its author William Pryce, a Redruth surgeon. Pryce, who began collecting information on mining when still a young man, spent much of his life within seven miles of Wendron, and his account of tin-streaming is probably based on what he saw near his home. Details of the streaming and dressing operations have therefore been taken from his work, and are supplemented by information from Carew and Borlase on stamping-mills, and from Henwood's papers of 1828 and 1873. Here it should be noted that the dressing techniques employed in Wendron depended very largely on the nature of the deposits being worked, and developed on very different lines to those employed elsewhere in Cornwall.

When the eighteenth-century streamers had bounded the land, or had obtained a lease (called a sett) or license from the mineral lord or the bounders, they would sink a hatch or timber-lined shaft to the bedrock, to ascertain the thickness and value of the tin-ground. From time to time as the work proceeded they would take a shovelful of stuff and wash off the lighter waste in water. From the tin-gravel left behind it was possible to judge whether the ground was worth working

or not. This process was known as vanning, and, on a specially-shaped shovel, is still practised in Cornwall today. If the ground was found to be worth working, the streamers would then dig a trench from the lowest part of their bounds, as near level as possible, to drain the water and waste from their workings. The overburden was then removed, while the workings were kept clear of water, either by scooping, or with a hand-pump, or with a rag-and-chain pump, or by means of a pump driven by a water-wheel. The tin-ground was shovelled on to a tye or inclined plane of boards (a forerunner of the modern sluice-box, widely used in Malaya), about four feet wide and nine feet long, and erected about four feet above the level of the bedrock. A cascade of water running over it served to separate and carry off the lighter waste, leaving the heavier tin-gravel to collect at the head of the tye. After this partial dressing the tinstuff was raised to ground level, and when sufficient had accumulated it was dressed again to make it fit for smelting. There were several ways of doing this, but the usual method was to make a gounce or strake, in which the smaller particles of tin-gravel were washed over again as in the tye, but using a smaller current of water and a larger degree of care and caution to prevent the finer particles from escaping in suspension in the water. The richest part of the tin-gravel accumulated near the upper end or head of the gounce, and was taken out separately, while the poorer part lying towards the lower end or tail was dressed over again until all the tin-gravel had been taken out. This was done by sifting it in a wood or wire sieve, the lighter part being carefully skimmed off and laid aside to work over again. The sand containing the smallest grains of tin, which passed through the wire sieve, was then put into another and more finely woven horse-hair sieve called a dilluer. This was shaken up and down and from side to side in a kieve (say *keeve*) or barrel of water, which resulted in the small and light particles of waste becoming suspended in the water. The sieve was then tilted to allow the waste to pass out and settle in the kieve, leaving ore fit for smelting in the dilluer. Some of the nodules or lumps of tin were fit for smelting as they came out of the gounce, but those mixed with waste were put with the low-grade refuse from the tails of the tye and gounce, and were sent to a stamping-mill to be stamped and dressed like mine tin.

Meanwhile, as the work proceeded upstream, the waste, stones and soil were thrown back over the worked-out

Excavating for tin. *Clive Carter*

Vanning a sample of black tin: the late Ross Polkinghorne.

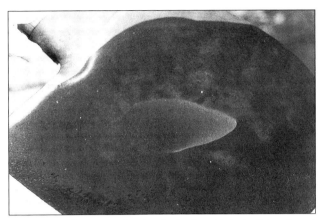

Black tin sample on a vanning shovel. The tin oxide is the light coloured toungue at the right.

dug out of a stream-works was to be placed. On conviction the fine for breaking this law was £10, half of which was to be paid to the King and the other half to the inhabitants of the port, town or haven bringing the action. Besides being one of the earliest of our anti-pollution laws, the Act contains the earliest mention of what would now be called a catch-pit or slimes dam, and although it may have been difficult to enforce, it became part of Stannary Law. The Convocation of 1752 confirmed the law against damage by stream-works and ruled that tinners who broke it should be fined £5, of which half went to the Duke of Cornwall (as mineral lord) and half to the person aggrieved, in addition to which the tinner was, on conviction, to be liable for all costs and damages. The reduction in the fine could suggest that the Act was successful in its intentions; and 'catch-pit clauses' are sometimes found in mining and streaming leases of the time.[28]

Carew noted that the stamping-mill of the fifteen eighties was a device 'where three, and in some places six, great logges of timber, bound at the ends with yron, and lifted vp and downe by a wheele, driuen with Water, doe break it smaller.' From the stamping-mill the ore passed to a crazing-

ground or were piled in heaps at the side of the excavation. In the sixteenth century, although Mother Nature was more likely to be the culprit, the washing of tin was thought to have caused the silting-up of rivers and harbours around the Cornish coast, and in 1531 an Act was passed making it unlawful to stream tin unless sufficient hatches and tyes were made at the ends of the buddles, into which all the rubbish

Rag and chain pump. *Clive Carter*

mill, 'which betweene two grinding stones, turned also with a water-wheele, bruseth the same to a fine sand.' However the use of wet stampers had already been adopted, rendering the crazing-mill unnecessary except for grinding the 'crust of their tayles' or coarser tailings. That the thrifty tinner would not wish to throw away a piece of equipment if it could still be used was shown by the fate of one such mill, which was built

into a stamps wall at Trelubbus. Here, in the middle of the last century, a roughly circular granite stone about three feet in diameter was found. Weighing about six hundredweights, it had a hole in the centre about five inches in diameter, directly below which was a roughly-cut slot, to enable it to be turned by a vertical spindle. The grinding surface was marked with concentric grooves, and the whole resembled a quern or ancient corn-mill, which would have been worked by water.[29]

Carew added that after the tin ore had passed through the stamps and crazing-mill it was 'made to fall by certayne

22

degrees one somewhat distant from another; vpon each of which, at euery discent, lyeth a greene turfe, three or four foote square and one foote thick.' On these the tinner would lay a quantity of stamped ore and would work it over with a shovel so that the light earth was washed away, leaving clean black tin on the turf. The ore thus collected was then washed in round shallow wooden dishes about two feet across; 'the

residue, after this often cleansing, they call black Tynne.' The best turves for dressing came from about two miles east of St Michael's Mount, a place which can be identified as Praa (say *pray*) Sands. The turves were dug up at low tide after removing a layer of sand; and the deposit of peat remaining can still be seen near high-water mark. In Wendron, too, there were ample peat deposits which would have served the purpose for dressing stream-tin, and which could also be dried and burned to recover the fine tin it had absorbed.

The upper stone from a crazing mill, used before stamps came into general use. *Justin Brooke*

Tin-stamps and dressing floors, 18th century. *Clive Carter*

In 1788 the stamping-mill usually had three upright beams, called lifters, made from ash timber six or seven inches square and about nine or ten feet long. They were armed at the bottom with large masses of iron called stamp-heads, weighing 140 lbs each. There were tongues of wood projecting from each lifter, and as the axle-tree rotated the wooden knobs or teeth fixed in it, called caps, lifted each lifter in turn and allowed it to fall. The ore was placed on an inclined plane called a pass, close to and sloping towards the bottom of the stamps. As the latter were lifted up, the ore slid down and underneath the first head, which partly crushed it. The second stamper was lifted an instant before the fall of the first, and the third before that of the second. The fall of the first forced part of the ore underneath the second, and that of the second underneath the third, while the fall of the third forced the crushed ore up against the grate. A stream of water kept the ore wet and the stamp-heads cool, and helped the crushed ore to pass through the holes in the grate. The grate was an iron plate a tenth of an inch thick and about a foot square, and a stamping-mill generally had several interchangeable grates, with holes varying in diameter from that of a reed to one of a small needle, from which one would be chosen according to the nature of the ore to be treated. The introduction of the interchangeable grate probably took place in the second half of the sixteenth century, concurrently with the introduction of wet stamping and the abandonment of the crazing mill. By the middle of the nineteenth century a modification had been introduced to the stamping-mill, whereby the fine sand produced by the stamps was carried by the swell of the water over a thin-edged board or weir, which was known as a flasher. Stamps using flashers were sometimes called 'flosh stamps'.[30]

Dressing operations also became more complicated in the century before 1788. Pryce noted that the crushed ore which passed through the holes in the grate ran into the forepit, where the rough ore, called the crop, was caught. The rest passed to the middle pit and from thence into a third pit, the ore in these pits being called slimes. As soon as the first pit was full its contents were carried to a buddle, which was a pit seven feet long, three feet wide, and two feet deep. The dresser, or a stout boy, standing in the buddle, spread the ore in small ridges on the line of the flow of water, on a board called a jagging-board, which was fixed across the head of the buddle. The water washed the lighter parts of the ore from the ridges, while the ore was moved to and fro on the board with a shovel, to separate the lighter waste and to carry it off in suspension in the water. Here it can be noted that 'jag' is a Cornish word meaning to jog or jolt, and if, as the writer suspects, the dresser occasionally tapped the jagging-board with his shovel, to assist the ore to spread out more evenly, we have in Cornwall, and possibly in Wendron, the forerunner of the modern shaking-table, which works on the same principle.

When the buddle was full the upper and richer third of the partly-dressed ore, lying nearest the jagging-board and called the crop, was taken out and stirred in a kieve with a shovel. This operation, which was called tozing or tossing, made the lighter impurities become suspended in the water. The side of the kieve was then banged with a mallet, an operation known as packing, which made the black tin fit for smelting settle at the bottom. A mechanised form of this process was in use at Geevor and South Crofty mines until a few years ago, and samples of black tin concentrated in this way often contain small splinters of wood from the inside of the kieve. The 'foul water' on the top of the kieve was poured off, and the sordes or mud which had settled on top of the black tin was skimmed off and put on one side to be washed again. While this was being done, the ore deposited in the middle of the buddle was being put through the same treatment as the crop or head, while the lower part was put into the kieve for tozing and packing.

The contents of the second and third pits, which

Dressing tin ore on a buddle. From an old print.

contained the smaller and lighter parts of the ore, mixed with a greater quantity of earth and stone, were known as slimes. They were carried by boys, mostly under fourteen years of age, to a small circular pit, from which they were transferred to a semicircular pit at the head or pednan of the trunk. A boy stirred the slimes in the pednan with a little shovel; and the tin and waste, in suspension, flowed over a board about ten inches deep, and into the body of the trunk. The trunk was a pit lined with boards, ten feet long, three feet wide, and eight inches deep. The ore which settled in the fore-part of the trunk was carried off to be framed, while that which settled lower down was moved forward to be put through the trunk again.

The frame was made in two parts, body and head. A small stream of water fell on the head of the frame and washed the ore, which was laid out in little ridges on a flat piece of wood, called a lippet, similar to a jagging-board. The lippet was nearly horizontal, and the water ran so slowly over it that by moving the slime tin to and fro with a light hand, and 'exposing it cautiously to the water with a semicircular rake' or raking movement, all the sordes were washed away and the tin, though very fine, remained on the frame near the head. When the tin was found to be sufficiently clean the

Buddling. *Clive Carter*

body of the frame, which was fixed on two iron bearings called melliers, one at each end, was turned from a horizontal to a vertical position, allowing the tin to run off into a coffer or box. When the coffer was full its contents were tozed, sifted and packed. They were then carried back to the frame and cazed, which was done by stopping the lower end of the frame with slime or turf, so that the water would be quite still and the tin would be enabled to settle more easily in the frame. After this second framing the tin in the coffer was taken to the kieve for tozing, skimming and packing. Borlase remarked that it was surprising to see with what ease, cheapness and regularity all these complicated processes were performed.[31] However, the simple methods at first employed in dressing tin-gravels only recovered the coarser grades, and much of the finer material was carried off in suspension.

Pryce noted that there was another kind of stream-works, that which dressed the leavings and refuse from stamping-mills. This was carried down by the rivers to the lower grounds, and after some years lying and collecting there yielded some money to the dressers. They were called lappiors, 'I suppose from the Cornish word *lappior*, which, signifying a Dancer, is applied to them, from the boys and girls employed in this work, and moving up and down in the buddles to separate the Tin from the refuse, with naked feet like to the ancient Dancers.'[32]

Once it had been dressed ready for smelting, the tin-gravel became known as stream-tin or 'good moor tin'. As well as being more easily obtained than black tin or 'good mine tin', stream-tin was considered to be the best sort, as it was purer and freer from sulphur and arsenic than mine tin, and was consequently easier to smelt. When smelted it yielded a superior quality of metal which, on solidifying after smelting, was heated almost to melting-point and dropped on to a hard surface, where it instantly divided into small striated masses. This was called grain tin, which was used in the Middle Ages in alloys for bells, for pewter and solder, for cannons, and for tinning the insides of copper and brass cooking-pots. It was later used in tin-plate, in making tin-foil, in organ-pipes, and, in compounds, as a mordant for dyes. In the fifteen-eighties two pounds by weight of good mine tin would yield a pound of metal, a grade of 50 per cent, whereas eighty pounds of good moor tin would yield fifty-two pounds of metal, equivalent to a grade of 65 per cent. By 1730 good mine tin yielded 55 to 65 per cent of metal, due to an improvement in tinners' methods, though it was not stated whether the tinners were miners or smelters. In 1788 stream-tin fetched 10s to 12s per cwt more than mine tin.[33]

In 1828 Henwood, then a clerk at the Perran Foundry at Perran ar Worthal, noted that considerable modifications but little improvement had been made in dressing stream and mine tin during the preceding half-century. Although the principle on which it was conducted was nearly the same, the modes of applying it were in many cases very different, and practices varied from one district to another. In general he wrote, it should be assumed that tin ores were carried by the miner (and by inference the streamer as well) through all the operations needed to make them fit for smelting. However, the time-honoured practice of selling rough tin ore to a 'bargain buyer' for stamping and dressing was still current at the time he wrote, and continued to be a feature of the tin-mining scene for another fifty or sixty years. He added in 1873 that the detrital deposits of Cornwall were not quite exhausted, but that some of them recently worked had been found to have been worked before. Throughout the neighbourhood of the river Cober trout thrived in every rivulet and pool (they still do), and water-worn granules of exceedingly pure gold up to the size of a small pea were very occasionally found. At this time, according to two smelters, the annual production of grain tin was only about fifty tons for the whole county.[34]

An illustration of the importance of tin-streaming to the

local economy was given in July 1836, when a meeting was convened in Helston. Its purpose was to consider what action to take over a claim made on behalf of Lady Basset of Tehidy to the right of waters in the parish of Wendron, and to divert them from the tin-streams on the moors and from the ancient mines in which they had been used, for a new mine called Wheal Friendship in the moor west of Porkellis. The interested parties were the tin-streamers, who with their families numbered nearly three hundred people, or about a fifth of the population of the parish. They feared that if the water were diverted they would lose their livelihoods. Between two and three hundred people turned up on the appointed day, and as they could not be accommodated at the Angel Inn or the Town Hall, George Concanen addressed the crowd from an upstairs window at Mr Lenderyou's. A

petition to Lady Basset was drawn up and signed by over 220 people (the *Mining Journal* gave a figure of 270), and a copy of it was printed in the local papers. Grylls & Hill, the Helston solicitors acting for Lady Basset, replied the following week that only one man, Thomas Bolitho, without family, had been thrown out of work in consequence of the diversion of the water, and he was now working elsewhere on Porkellis Moor. The Bassets had enjoyed the water in question for centuries, and the late Lord De Dunstanville and Basset had drawn rents from it all his life. The problem solved itself in March 1838, when Wheal Friendship was closed and its equipment, including a 19 feet diameter water-wheel with 3 feet breast (the cause of the trouble) together with 6½ fathoms of pumps, was put up at auction.[35]

To conclude this chapter it is worth placing on record the names of two non-mining people who have noted facts which

Tozing – the final process in dressing slime tin.   *Clive Carter*

appear to have escaped the notice of the scientific men who have examined the area. Firstly, the late R. J. Cunnack, a Helston business-man, noted that the tin ore from mines in and around Porkellis Moor was much intermixed with specular iron ore, locally called 'glist', which caused difficulties in dressing. In attempting to get rid of it the mines lost considerable quantities of tin in slimes, to the advantage of the streamers, who made a tolerable livelihood from dressing them.[36] Secondly, the late S. J. Wills, a Wendron schoolmaster, wrote that the best stream-tin in the district came from the exact bottom of the valley in the bed of the stream at Polgear, at the foot of Nine Maidens Downs, where wolfram was also plentiful.[37] There are no records of any sales of that mineral from this area.

CHAPTER THREE
STAMPING MILLS

IN WENDRON THE working of alluvial deposits and the waste from stamping-mills went on side by side for centuries, those streams working waste being mostly situated on the river Cober below Trenear. The late Dr A. K. Hamilton Jenkin recorded that the first stamping-mill in Duchy land, and possibly the earliest in Cornwall, was erected before 1493, when John Trenere, freeman, held such a mill in Trenere Wolas (Lower Trenear). His neighbour in 1500 had a newly-built 'skof myll or scoffe myll'. Considerable research has failed to produce a description of such a mill, and it has been suggested that the name may be derived from the Cornish *scovan*, the rich part of a tin lode, and would thus give a clue to the approximate date of the beginning of lode-mining in the parish. However, the writer inclines to the view that the name comes from the Cornish *scovva*, a shelter, shade or refuge, and that in fact the scoff mill was no more than a corn mill protected by walls and a roof. This view is supported by the fact that the scoff mill at Trenear was put up for sale in 1812, a fate unlikely to have overtaken any temporary structure built three centuries earlier.[38]

It is unlikely that the full number of stamping-mills in Wendron, or all their sites, will ever be known. A survey made in 1650 lists a crazing-mill and two stamping-mills at Trenere Wolas, two stamping-mills at Garlidna, and two at Calvadnack. A map from the second half of the eighteenth century shows the sites of no less than eighteen stamping-mills on or near Porkellis Moor, of which four were on the stream running through Medlyn Moor and four on the tributary of the Cober rising near Carnkie. Besides noting these stamps the site of a grist mill called Mellen Beblow (streams mill) is shown between Viscar and Little Garlidna.[39] Modern maps show the building as one of the three Garlidna farms, and the mill is now a dwelling-house. A field below Little Garlidna farm, long known as Stamps Field, indicates one use to which the land has been put in the past, and level and sandy soil of the three fields in the bottom of the valley show that on the cessation of stamping the dumps of waste sand were spread out and the land reclaimed. On the adjoining tenement of Viscar the Tithe Apportionment of 1840 lists five fields with Stamps in their names; and elsewhere in the parish a further fifteen. Other references to streaming or mining are provided by such fields as Pullrose (from the Cornish *polrose*, a pit for a water-wheel) on Boquio and Audit (adit or aqueduct) fields on Carnebone, Halabezack, Lezerea and Lancarrow.

Enough records have survived to show that at times there was a surplus of stamping capacity in the parish, since two of the stamping-mills leased were described as dilapidated, and

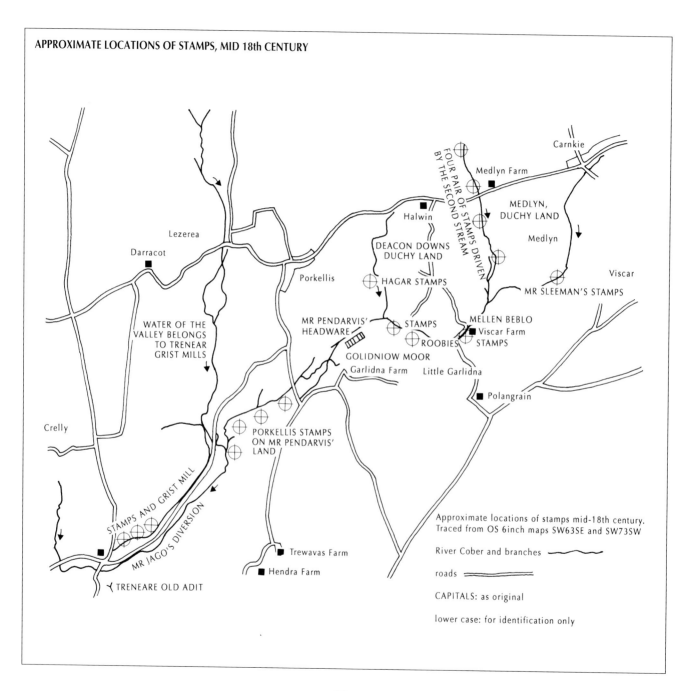

APPROXIMATE LOCATIONS OF STAMPS, MID 18th CENTURY

Carnkie

Medlyn Farm

FOUR PAIR OF STAMPS DRIVEN BY THE SECOND STREAM

MEDLYN, DUCHY LAND

Halwin

Medlyn

Lezerea

DEACON DOWNS DUCHY LAND

Viscar

Darracot

Porkellis

HAGAR STAMPS

MR SLEEMAN'S STAMPS

WATER OF THE VALLEY BELONGS TO TRENEAR GRIST MILLS

MR PENDARVIS' HEADWARE

STAMPS

MELLEN BEBLO

Viscar Farm
STAMPS

ROOBIES

GOLIDNIOW MOOR

Garlidna Farm

Little Garlidna

Polangrain

Crelly

PORKELLIS STAMPS ON MR PENDARVIS' LAND

STAMPS AND GRIST MILL

MR JAGO'S DIVERSION

Trewavas Farm

Hendra Farm

TRENEARE OLD ADIT

Approximate locations of stamps mid-18th century.
Traced from OS 6inch maps SW63SE and SW73SW

River Cober and branches

roads

CAPITALS: as original

lower case: for identification only

32

Old water-wheel and stamps. Note worn gearing. *Justin Brooke*

another, at Coldwind on Lezerea, was demolished before a corn-mill was built on part of its site. Coldwind Stamps were leased in 1732 to Thomas Watts of Wendron, victualler and tinner, for seven years, at £15 annually, payable quarterly. In 1743 they passed to Richard Carne, an illiterate tinner, who took them for another seven years, but whose quarterly rents only amounted to £9 per annum. The land on which they stood ultimately passed into the hands of the Rev. John

Trevenen of Creed. In August 1832 his executors contracted with a Helston carpenter named William Pascoe to erect 'a good firm and substantial double water grist mill and dwelling-house, the walls of which are to be of stone and the roof slated.' The house is now known as Flushing Farm, taking its name from a nearby field, and the leat which fed the water-wheel of the mill can still be traced along the hillside.[40]

The water for Coldwind Stamps was diverted from Tolcarne and from the stream below Burras. In 1727 the water from Coldwind Stamps was carried by a new leat to Cross Hole Stamps, of which the earliest record is from 1689. It then went to Lezerea South and West Stamps, which were working at least from 1727 to 1783. The two pairs of stamps on Lezerea were owned by Samuel Enys of Penryn, who leased them in March 1696 to Edward Trevenen of Crowan, tinner. They were formerly held by Thomas Tresilian of Wendron, gentleman, and the new lessee, who also enjoyed a free supply of water, paid a yearly rent of £3 and undertook to maintain the leat, water-wheels, roofs, walls, and upstanders, while the lessor provided the stamp-heads. About 1780 part of the water from Coldwind was diverted in another leat to Mr Glyn's headwear in Heath Moor, below Lezerea, where it was joined by Mr Hill's watercourse from Boswin. The water from the Lezerea Stamps was also divided, one part continuing in a leat to Mr Enys' Stamps an Pons (the bridge stamps) and thence into the river Cober above Porkellis Bridge. The other part went by launder to Park an Pons (the bridge field) Higher and Lower Stamping Mills, and from thence into the river.[41]

In the eighteen-nineties there was a vague tradition that the mill at Tolcarne Wartha (Upper Tolcarne) had once been a stamping-mill. From just below the mill a leat ran south-eastwards to White Alice Stamps, also known as Hill's Old Stamping Mill, near the present-day Wheal Rock farm. With Hagarowell Stamps these stamps were leased in July 1761 by John Hill of Trenethick to Benjamin Hearne, a Penryn merchant, and three tinners, namely William Trevarthen of Crowan and Samuel Eva and Thomas Watts of Wendron . The stamps were leased for £6 per annum, and, being dilapidated, were to be rebuilt by the lessees, who were responsible for the maintenance of the plant, other than the water-wheels, axletrees, launders, thatch and buddle-heads. The stamps gave their name to Stamps Moor, to the south of the site. Hagarowell Stamps lay to the south, on the other side of the hill, near the bottom of the lane of that name and not far from the Carnkie branch of the river Cober. These were leased to John Hill to the same parties at an annual rent of £12. The lease for both properties was for six years; and Hagarowell Stamps included 'all Plotts, Buddles, Budling Places, fframeing places, Slime Pits, Wayes, Waters, Water-courses, Headwears, Leats, Ponds, Pooles, Rivulets, and Springs of Water to the same belonging and used and enjoyed to and with the same', showing that in the preceding two centuries considerable work had been done on the site by John Thomas of Constantine and his successors, as noted in Chapter 6.[42]

The earliest reference to a stamping-mill on Porkellis Moor yet seen by the writer is from 1634, when one was specifically excluded from a lease of the adjoining land, granted by Samuel Pendarves to Peter Hill alias Combellack.[43] The mill was probably at or near the site occupied in September 1822 by Porkellis Stamping Mill, which lay west of Porkellis and 'nigh a tin work called Vean Vorose', a

Wheelpit, Bodilly Consols, Wendron. *Justin Brooke*

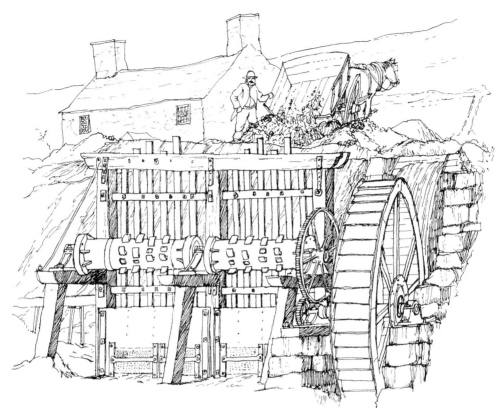

Salena stamps. *Clive Carter*

corruption of Mean Vrose (great rock). The stamps were leased by Richard Gerveys Grylls and Humphrey Millett Grylls to Ralph Allen Daniel of Trelissick and Thomas Hocken of Stithians, gentlemen, who may have been the trustees appointed by the cost-book company formed to work Wheal Foster, noted elsewhere. The stamps were then in ruins, and the lessees undertook to repair them.[44]

Lower Porkellis Stamping Mills, held by John Bolitho (deceased), were leased in February 1746 by Thomas Glynn of Helston to William and John Pasmore of the same town, William Knuckey and Henry Bodilly, for 21 years at an

annual rent of six guineas, payable quarterly. The lease provided that the lessees should maintain the walls, thatch, coverings, leats, dams, hedges, floodgates and headwears, while the lessor required that when the lease ran out the lessees should hand over 'the Wheel Axle, Axle trees, upstanders, Goosework, Launders, and upper ffloodgates', which were apparently the lessor's responsibility to maintain. In 1767 the property was found to be in a most ruinous state, and the two Pasmores, William Tremayne of Phillack and two Wendron tinners named Samuel Evans and Francis Hill bought it. In February 1769 they undertook to repair the stamping-mill and to carry the water from it to the Trenear

A mortar-stone, formerly used in stamping tin. *Justin Brooke*

Mill adit (leat). This shows that the stamps must have been some distance below Porkellis Bridge, west of the village, as the tail of the Trenear adit was at the foot of the hill below Carthvean and some three hundred yards south-west of the bridge.[45]

Just below Trenear there were three sets of stamps. The most modern of them, of which traces still remain, was at Salena, and appears to have been erected towards the end of the last century near the site of some stamps at work in 1790. The new set may have been intended to succeed or to compete with Bodilly Stamps, which lay in the valley south of the farm of that name. These were let for £12 per annum in 1781 to Richard and James Goldsworthy by Christopher Wallis, a Helston attorney. Difficulties over the water-course to the stamps were overcome in 1796 by referring back to an original deed of 1716, showing John Rogers of Penrose to be its owner. The stamps were held in 1840 by the Wheal Lovell company and in 1851 by the Trumpet Consols company, and appear to have been at work when the Ordnance Survey mapped the area in the late eighteen-seventies.[46] Just below Wendron church lay the Glebe Stamps, locally known as Hangman's Stamps, which dated from before 1790 and which were held in 1893 by Samuel Rogers.[47] At Coverack (locally

36

Glebe Stamps, late 19th century. West Wendron Consols' engine house is in the background. The site is still recognisable today.
Royal Institution of Cornwall

pronounced carvrack) Bridges there were two sets of stamps, those on the Sithney side of the river being called Sithney Coverack to distinguish them from the Wendron ones. Their site was later cleared and levelled, and now (1993), after many vicissitudes, forms the vehicle park for small industrial units in the nearby buildings. Although there are now no traces of the stamps the leat which fed the water-wheel can be traced some distance up the valley. The stamps on the Wendron side of the river continued to work well into the present century, and foundations of buildings and a pit for the water-wheel can still be seen. The stamps were on or close to the site of an earlier stamping-mill and burning-house, which, together with the leavings and halvans at Trenethick Wood mine, were put up for sale in March 1809, when the cost-book company working that mine went into liquidation.[48]

Still lower down the valley the stamps at Trelubbas Wollas (Lower Trelubbas) were owned by Henry Donston of Tregaddra in 1574, as noted below. At Trelubbas Wartha (Higher Trelubbas) there were two stamping-mills in 1782, which, with part of the tenement in which they lay, were leased by Arthur Holdsworth of Dartmouth to Thomas Wills of Helston. The property lay adjacent to the New Blowing-House, the old one having been converted to a stamping-mill; and the whole had been built by John Johns. The lease was for 99 years for a consideration of £84, plus an annual rent of £2.5s. and a capon. The property can be identified from the description in the lease as the modern Trewartha, and one of its stamping-mills may have been at Coverack Bridges: 'all that land that leadeth from the house as the lane leadeth towards Helstone on the south part, and from thence as the hedge leadeth towards Coverack Bridge, and from thence as the River leadeth to the hedge of Trelubbas Wollas (the modern Trelubbas) together with the right and common of pasture, turf, and fuel, in Trelubbas Wartha Moor alias Coverack Moor.' A clause in the lease covered water, equipment, and a right to turn diverted water back into the river Cober.[49]

Trelubbas Stamps were held for a while up to 1840 by the three adventurers in Wheal Ann, which later became part of Trumpet Consols mine. In 1837 four tons of black tin were sold for £189.5s. as 'Trelubbas bargains', which suggests that the lessees of the stamps also acted as 'bargain buyers', buying parcels of partly-dressed stream tin and tin ore from tin-streams and small mines for further dressing and sale. The stamps were taken over by the Trumpet Consols company in 1851 and, as noted elsewhere, were later held by the Wendron Consols company.[50] A chimney shown on the 1880 Ordnance Survey map has long since disappeared, as have the wooden launders which carried the water across the rocky part of the hillside. Nevertheless, traces of the old leats and slimes ponds can still be seen. The best approach to the site, which is heavily overgrown, is by a path along the south bank of the river, which can be reached by a bridge near the council dump above Lowertown.

At Lowertown a set of stamps was erected by William Tremayne some years before 1792, when he sold 'all that well known Stamping Mill known as Lower Town Stamps' to George Fox of Perranwell. In addition to the £50 charged for the stamps a further charge of £1.3s.6d. was made for materials and sundries, while legal fees were £1. The materials included a kieve, the old ironwork of three kieves, two frames, two old wrought iron stamps heads weighing three-quarters of a hundredweight, two cast iron heads on the stamps, three lifters, four old frame millers (mellyers or bearings), a settling sarge (searge, a horse-hair sieve), and a stamps hammer. The annual outgoings were given as 5s. rent and £1 to cover conventionary rent, church and poor rates, and land-tax, the two last-named items being charged on the two heads of stamps. At Lowertown, and at Trannack on the Sithney side of the river, the Wheal Ann Stamping Mills were leased to W. Pasmore of Helston in 1794. Two further stamping-mills were erected about 1813, when Christopher

Coverack Bridges Stamps in the 1920s. On the extreme right is Tom Johns, a native of Breage, who managed the stamps, assisted by his son Thomas William Johns and two others. This view is full of fascinating detail. On the far left an unusually broad water wheel drives a set of stamps, rag frames are in the foreground and at the rear of the shed on the right is a round frame. Tom Johns is working a kieve. On the skyline is the Wheal Dream engine house and stack, part of Trumpet Consols, demolished in the 1940s. *Eric Edmonds.*

Wallis arranged to lease them to the adventurers in Polladras Downs Mine in Breage (which later became part of Wheal Vor), for 21 years at £30 per annum clear of all outgoings, plus a further £10 per annum if two new stamps were put up on the same plot. [51]

Less detail has survived about the stamping-mills on the Kennal or Tretheague river running down to Perran ar Worthal, though it is known that Mannerlew (Menerlue) Stamps were leased by Mr Basset of Tehidy in 1754.[52] In 1819 there were no less than 48 water-wheels on the river between Carnmenellis and Perran Wharf, of which six were used by the Kennal Vale Gunpowder Works and several more by the paper-mill and the hammer-mill.[53] On the eastern side of the parish, Treloar farm was leased in September 1766 by the Rev. William Sandys of St Minver to Thomas and John Chegwidden, father and son. The lease specifically excluded a stamping-mill being erected on a nearby stream, as well as the old walls, tin-house and 'plotts and conveniences for laying of casultyes and leavings and working the same', and provided access to the stamping-mill and to the tin-streams on the Moor.[54] A little further down the stream the stamps at Trussall were let to the adventurers of Trevenen Mine, and were put up for sale in November 1811. The exact site is not known, though it may have been in a field named Wheel Pit Croft in the Tithe Apportionment. On the western side of the stream lay Treloquithack Stamps. These were already at work in 1781, and in 1796 they were leased to William Pasmore of Helston. Their site was offered for sale Captain Perry of Treloquithack in September 1821 and February 1822. The plot adjoining the stamps was then 'a well-fenced and thriving plantation', and the stream of water which fed the stamps was leased to the Trevenen adventurers, of whose mine Captain Perry was manager, at a yearly rent of £2.[55]

On the west bank of the stream and a short distance south of Trussall, in the northern part of Grambla Wood, lay Wood Stamps, possibly the successor to Treloquithack Stamps. An ivy-covered chimney stands close to the lane leading to the site of the dressing-floors, which is marked on modern maps as Cornish Dairy, indicating the site's most recent use. The 1880 Ordnance Survey map shows a large oblong pond below the stamps site, of a kind which, with stream diversions to provide the necessary water-power, would have been its final use to catch the waste from the stamping-mill prior to treatment. After being held for some years by the Trumpet Consols company Wood Stamps were sold to the Wheal Lovell company in 1858. They were apparently still at work in 1893 under the ownership of Henry Rogers.[56]

CHAPTER FOUR
SMELTING

UNTIL THE ABOLITION of the coinage of tin in 1837 all black tin raised in Cornwall and Devon had to be smelted into tin metal, also known as white tin, and brought to a coinage town to be weighed, tested for purity, and taxed. The tin raised in the Wendron area was brought to Helston, which was the coinage town for the Stannary of Penwith and Kerrier, and where Coinage-Hall Street serves as a reminder of an ancient industry. The mode of testing the blocks of tin was to strike off a corner (in Norman-French *coign*), partly by cutting and partly by breaking, in order to prove the toughness and fineness of the metal.[57]

The most primitive of the furnaces used for smelting tin were known as Jews' houses, a number of which have been found in west Cornwall. Those found in Wendron include one at Tolcarne Wartha, where much partly-smelted tin was discovered, and another at Lezerea near the site of the stamps. The earliest form of these furnaces consisted of a narrow shallow pit over which sticks were piled crosswise on each other, as high as they would easily stand. Tin ore was then scattered on the pile, and the pile was set on fire. The oxygen in the tin oxide combined with the carbon from the burning wood, and the melted tin metal ran into the bottom of the pit, where it became mixed with the loose earth or sand. This necessitated a second smelting to remove the impurities.

Masses of tin thus formed were known as Jews' tin or Jews' bowls, and varied in size from a few ounces to eighty pounds.[58] A more recent variety of Jew's house, found near Penzance a century and a half ago, was in the form of an inverted cone, about three feet high and three feet wide at the top. The sides of the cone were of hard clay, and there was a hole at the bottom through which a blast of air from a bellows was conveyed to the fire, and another hole through which the molten tin flowed.[59]

In the Middle Ages the Jews' house developed into the blowing-house, and blowing-houses were set up in almost every area where alluvial tin was worked. By the fourteenth century they were in common use, most of them having been erected in high and exposed places so as to catch the wind. The fire-place or hearth of a blowing-house was built of massive blocks of stone, clamped together with iron. It was about six feet high, two feet square inside at the top and about fourteen inches square at the bottom. In later years it was flanked by two large bellows about eight feet long and two and a half feet wide at the widest part, which were worked by a water-wheel, such works being known as blowing-mills. The pipe or nose of each bellows was fixed ten inches from the bottom of the fire-place in a large sheet of wrought iron called the hearth-eye. Charcoal and black tin were placed in layers in the hearth, the charcoal was ignited, and the bellows were set to work, creating an intense heat which smelted the metal. The metal ran through a hole at the bottom of the hearth, four inches high and an inch and a half wide, and into a granite trough up to six and a half feet long and a foot wide, called a float. From here, while still molten, it was ladled into smaller troughs or moulds which, when full, contained about three hundred pounds of tin metal, and where it cooled and formed the block tin sold to commercial users after being coined. The hearth was set in a stone building with a thatched roof, and the blowing-houses were fancifully known as castles.[60] A pair of bounds on Halwin named Goon Castle and Dacum Downs suggests that there might have been a blowing-house there, conveniently situated to smelt tin raised from the tin-streams and shallow workings on Porkellis Moor.

Blowing-houses were employed largely for the reduction of alluvial tin, in contrast to the concentrates from mine ore, which, from the early eighteenth century, were smelted in the then relatively new reverberatory furnaces. Blowing-houses often gave their name to local features; and one of the earliest recorded ones was in Wendron. Here, in 1337, there was a 'Blouwinghouse apud Polmarth', near the modern Carnmenellis hamlet, which was let to Thomas Adthelyn at an annual rent of two shillings.[61] Ten years later it was let to Laurence Hobbe for a fine of 3s.4d. on renewal, and an annual rent of a shilling. Hobbe, it is recorded, also held the toll of tin in the district, for which he paid £5.6s.8d. a year. He apparently enjoyed the privilege of taking game as well.[62]

About 1550 Leland noted he had travelled about four miles from Godolphin Hall to Trewedneck (Trannack), where Thomas Godolcan, Sir William's younger son, 'hath made an exceedingly fair blo-house mille in the rokky valley thereby.' This is likely to have been the ruined blowing-house visited in June 1811 by Christopher Wallis with a view to putting it in order. The other blowing-houses in the district at the time cannot be positively located, though in 1619 a case was reported in Helston where some tin stolen from a blowing-house was found to have been re-smelted at Castle Hill, near the Almshouses.[63] In 1650 there were blowing-houses at Seworgan, Trenere Wolas and Mooreknapp (possibly the modern Kenap), and six blowing-mills at Polmarth, while at Halvewither (possibly Halwin) a blowing-house had been abandoned. In 1659-60 there were still two blowing-houses 'near Helston', and in 1730 there were three in Wendron. Of the former, one was owned in 1619 by John Gwavas, whose name is preserved in the hamlet on the Sithney side of the river Cober, opposite Lowertown, and the other was owned by a Mr Hunckin. The site of one of these may have been near an ancient fortification called Castle Teen Urn (or Hern), above Lowertown, where accumulations of slag containing particles of metallic tin were found in the last century.[64] The blowing-house at Gweek had its own stamping-mill; both were mentioned in a deed of 1695. In December 1803 it was described as a convenient and well-situated blowing-house when a 99-year lease of it was offered for sale by private contract.[65] Lastly, in the eighteenth century, there were two blowing-houses at Trelubbas Wartha, already noticed.

Besides using the local blowing-houses, the tin-streamers of the eighteenth and nineteenth centuries had others to which to sell their produce. Some of the black tin from the Wendron area went to the Calenick smelter near Truro and to the Chyandour smelter in Penzance. They were by no means the nearest available, and the reasons for their choice must remain a matter for conjecture;[66] possibly they gave a better price for stream tin.

CHAPTER FIVE
BOUNDS AND BOUNDING

THE EARLIEST RECORD of any custom in Cornwall (and Devon) of working for tin on the lands of others is found in the Charter granted to the tinners by King John in 1201. This confirmed their right at all times, freely and quietly, without the disturbance of any man, to dig tin and turf to smelt it, anywhere in the moors and fees of bishops, abbots and earls, as they had been accustomed. They could also cut wood for smelting tin, and divert water-courses for their works in the Stannaries, as by ancient custom they were wont to do.[67]

In past centuries, before any ground could be prospected or worked for tin, whether stream or lode, it was customary to mark out its corners, a practice known as bounding. This was done by cutting turves and placing them at the corners or angles of the ground to be worked, three to six turves to each corner. Usually two pits were cut in the ground at each corner, about a foot wide and deep. In a 'Bal or cluster of mines', where there were numerous bounds adjoining one another, some corners had four or six pits; and corners with pits cut at an obtuse angle were called train-corners. The bound marks were renewed annually on a specific day by the toller or bounder, who would take a turf or shovelful of soil from the hole from which the turves had originally been cut and put it on the pile of turves. Sometimes stones were used to make bound-marks.

Such areas of bounded ground might be as small as a few perches or extend over several acres. Bounds were in wastrel or unenclosed land, though they could also be cut in several or enclosed land, provided that the land had been bounded before it was enclosed.[68] A bounded area was known as a pair of bounds, and cutting its corner-marks was called pitching. Bounds generally had four corners, north-east, south-east, south-west and north-west, and were usually described in writs of possession and in leases in that order. If the bounded area had five or more sides the additional triangles of land were called side-bounds, and their limits were described separately.

About the sixteenth century mineral lords began to exercise a right to place a workman in each pair of bounds on their land, and to make this a condition of granting a lease to a party wishing to work bounded land.[69] About the same time a distinction arose between mine and stream bounds, the latter not necessarily being on a stream of water. The corners of both were cut in the same way, though in the Stannary of Penwith and Kerrier the corner-marks of mine-bounds were inside the boundary, and in stream-bounds on the outside, a refinement which sometimes puzzled the mineral owner.[70] Mine-bounds, as their name implied, permitted deep mining by shafts and adits, while stream-bounds could only be worked as far down as the bedrock. Sometimes the same area was bounded by different parties for mine and for stream working.

By an Ordinance of 1546 bounders recorded their bounds in the Stannary Courts, which dealt with all matters concerning tin-streaming and mining from the end of the fifteenth century. The oldest surviving Court records are from 1503. A Commission held in 1525 recognised bounders and their obligation to enter the description of newly-cut bounds at a Stannary Court, while the Stannary Convocation of 1637 ordered that details of the locations, limits and intended workings of bounds should be entered and proclaimed at the Stannary Court in whose jurisdiction the bounds lay.[71] The 1688 Convocation added that when any new bounds were entered at the Court they should be openly proclaimed in Court at the next session after cutting and at the two Courts following before writs of possession of the 'bounds or tin-work' could be granted. In the meantime details of the bounds had to be posted in some open place in the Court until the writ of possession had been granted. Furthermore, the person pitching the bounds was obliged to serve notice of such pitching on the owner of the land, or on his agent. Finally, in 1752, the last Stannary Convocation to be held ordered that the owner of the land or his agent should be given at least three months' notice of an intention to pitch bounds, so that he might have an opportunity of cutting them and working them himself.[72]

From the middle of the sixteenth century, and possibly even earlier, bounds were cut for the use of three or four people, often including the mineral owner. Having acquired a joint title to a piece of ground, and having thus prevented any complications arising in the event of the death of one or more of their number, they proceeded to 'set and let' or sub-let the ground to individuals or small groups of tinners willing to work specified pitches within the bounds, or the whole bounds. To overcome the problem of illiteracy the lease would be read out to the tinners at the beginning of each working year, and an endorsement was made on the lease of the date and place at which each reading took place. Towards the end of the century tinners would make their marks on the lease or sign it if they were able, the head of each gang or pare, known as the taker, signing it for himself and for a specified number of men to be employed on his pitch.[73]

As time progressed more formal arrangements began to be made between mineral lords and tin-streamers, and instead of a memorandum between the lord's toller and the streamer, leases containing legally enforceable covenants became more usual in the second half of the eighteenth century. These covered not only tin-streaming but also streams and leats, and often specified which stamping-mills were to be used. Meanwhile, the giving of twenty-four hours' notice to the owners of tin-works or buddles of a wash of black tin was confirmed by a Stannary Court held in Helston in 1616.[74] This gave all those entitled to a share of the black tin a chance to collect it as soon as it had been divided.

Once pitched and recorded, bounds had the nature of chattels real, and were capable of being transferred or leased by deed or by word of mouth. The naming of bounds was at the whim of the bounders, though in the sixteenth century only the larger works were given a name,[75] in Cornish or English or a mixture of the two. Bounds not given a name were referred to by their location, as, for instance, the one recorded in Wendron in the eighteenth century as 'A Bounds nigh Peter Dowa's Dwelling-house, the south-west corner lying nigh a Tyn Mine called Pryor's Branch'.[76] The oldest named bounds in the Wendron district of which the writer has found a record is Trewen Tin-Work, which is likely to have been on or near the stream below the modern Trewennack. At a Stannary Court held in Helston in 1515 James Erisy (who had been Sheriff of Cornwall two years earlier) and others complained that Thomas de Seynt Aubyn and others had entered the work with force and arms, had

WHEAL RUBY TIN BOUNDS - 1838

worked the tin found there, and had taken it away. A jury of six men was appointed by the Court to hear the case at the next session, of which no record remains.[77]

At first, bounds were worked by tinners who each contributed labour and goods or money towards the working, and who shared the black tin they raised. Later, bounds were divided into doles (or fractions) representing as many as there were men working in them. These doles could be bought and sold like any other kind of property, and by the middle of the eighteenth century the custom of outsiders holding bounds or shares in bounds was widespread and well understood. In 1749, for instance, a total of 28 pairs of bounds in Wendron were renewed by Philip Tocker and John Matthew for the

Boundary stone on Garlidna, with 'B' indicating the boundary of Mr Basset's property. *Justin Brooke*

executors of Madam (Elizabeth) Hill, late of Helston, who had recently died.[78] Early in the nineteenth century shares in bounds came to be advertised for sale in the Cornish weekly papers. By this time they were becoming sub-divided, sometimes into very small or disparate fractions, as happened with mine shares. It appears that they were being regarded as investments, since there are indications that the landowning and moneyed classes, and not necessarily only the mineral lords, were accumulating shares in bounds on a large scale, either by purchase or (as one suspects) as security for loans. For instance, in May 1811 an auction was held in Helston of a portfolio of some 120 pairs of bounds and shares in bounds, not only in Wendron but also in Gwennap, Perranzabuloe, Redruth and St Agnes, evidently the property of a single owner. Then again, in January 1815 and on several subsequent occasions Messrs Grylls, Borlase and Scott, the Helston solicitors, advertised to sell by private contract a number of shares in bounds in Wendron, Breage, Lelant, Ludgvan, St Hilary, St Ives, Sithney, Towednack and Zennor, the thirty-four lots probably forming part of a deceased estate. The shares of bounds in Wendron included Bounds Bean, Coledna, the whole of a pair of stream bounds in Colvener alias Skidner Moor, Goon Castell and Dacum Downs, Polhigey Stream, and Wheal Ruby bounds, the bounding of the last-named going back to 1738. In those far-off days auctioneers also acted as share-dealers, and as there were no places where buyers and sellers of shares in bounds (or mines) could meet, they had to rely on public auctions or sales by tender or private contract. Grylls, Borlase and Scott played an important part in arranging such sales.[79]

Over the centuries the rights and obligations of bounders became progressively more complicated. The Stannary Convocation of 1688, amended by the Convocation Act of 1752, confirmed the rights of bounders to take up bounds cut by others but not worked. By the 1830s it had become generally assumed that bounds could be kept alive either by continuous working with annual renewal, or by annual renewal when unworked. About 1834 Captain Henry Crease, of whom we shall hear later, claimed, as Duchy lessee, the right to grant leases or setts in bounded land. Matters came to a head in 1836, when John Silvester of Helston, landlord of the Star Inn in that town and a former buddle-boy, advertised in the *Mining Journal* that he was agent for the tin-bounders in the Manor and Parish of Helston in Kerrier, which included part of Wendron. The owners and proprietors he represented, who had the exclusive right to grant leases of bounded land, were ready to grant leases or licenses to any respectable adventurers. He cautioned all persons against taking any sett or license from Henry Crease without prior application to the bounders. Mines then working in Wendron allegedly without the consent of the latter included Wheal Widden, Ruby and Garlidna, Treloar and Crowgey, and Balmynheer. The advertisement was witnessed by Frederick Hill of Helston, Silvester's solicitor, and a letter signed by Silvester, which appeared in print at the same time, stated that his father, grandfather, uncle, and he himself, had all been agents of the former lessees of the Duchy tin-dues, Messrs. Donnithorne and Smith, for fifty years and upwards.[80]

The advertisement led to considerable correspondence. Other writers claimed that Silvester had been employed by Captain Crease to collect dues, but that he had been discharged from his position of toller when his employer discovered that he had been acting as the bounders' agent while employed by Edward Smith, which gave a colour in some instances to bound claims. Captain Crease's solicitors, a London firm, replied in an advertisement in the *Mining Journal* and the Cornish papers, repeating that their client, alone, had a good title to the minerals he had farmed from the Duchy. It was later suggested that Silvester and Hill should bring an action at law to recover any one lease of bounds, or bring an action to recover bound dues from any adventurer who had not pledged himself by deed or

agreement to pay them, but they did not take the hint.[81]

The situation with regard to bounds was still unsatisfactory, however, and in 1839 proposals were made for legislation to extinguish unworked bounds kept up by annual renewal, unless they were registered at the Stannary Court by a certain date. It was also proposed that such bounders' rights could be bought out at a valuation, but the scheme failed to find support.[82] The dissatisfaction felt in mining circles at the time was reflected in the various lawsuits over bounded land in other parts of the county.[83] Bounding was nevertheless falling into disuse, and by 1855 it had from various causes become 'comparatively inoperative'. The main reason for this was a ruling of the Court of Queen's Bench in 1847, in the cause of Rogers v Brenton. Canon Rogers of Penrose, near Helston (after whom Canon's Town in St Erth was named), a leading local landowner, bounder, and owner of mineral rights in the Helston area, claimed the right to the tin in Ruby Bounds, which lay in part of the land leased to Wheal Ruby and Garlidna Mines, in Wendron, of which Captain William Brenton, the defendant, was manager. The plaintiff showed that the bounds had occasionally been worked and that dues had been paid, and that from 1823 to 1842 they had been unworked. Thereafter they had only been worked for a few months. The bounds had been renewed annually for many years. The Court held that the bounding custom was reasonable insofar as it permitted bounds to continue as long as the minerals in them were being worked, but that this custom was not so when it allowed unworked bounds to be kept alive by annual renewal. This decisively settled that a bounder who did not work his bounds had no interest in them, as had been the case centuries earlier, and that Canon Rogers had no claim on Captain Brenton. The tedium of the hearing, which was the last of a number which had dragged on over several years, was relieved by one witness who, during an examination of the bounding custom, stated that the parish church and cemetery of Helston were then actually situated within tin bounds.[84] Clearly the grave-digger was taking no chances!

Following the discontinuance of bounding the tin-streams and openworks continued to be worked under licenses or leases, either by individuals, or by simple partnerships keeping no accounts, or on the more formal cost-book system. No limited company appears to have been formed solely to work a tin-stream in the district until 1912, though in 1855 a joint-stock company (forerunner of the limited liability company and a rarity for the district) was proposed. Allegedly on the cost-book system but bearing none of the hallmarks of that type of concern, it was in 20,000 £1 shares, payable in full on allotment and without further liability. Promoted by two Londoners named Williams and Nicholson, it was given the grandiose title of The Wendron United China-Clay and Peat Works, Tin Mining and Streaming Company, the longest name ever given to a Wendron mining venture. The land on which it intended to work consisted of about 400 acres on Lancarrow estate in the northern part of the parish, part of which had been granted by the freeholder for 31 years and part by the Duchy for 21 years, 'at 1-15th dues in lieu of annual rent'. Large quantities of stream tin worth £75 per ton were said to have been found under large beds of first-rate china clay. A second lease covered the whole sett of the adjoining Hope, Polgear and Lancarrow Tin and Copper Mining Company, whose engine and plant had been bought by the new concern, and whose shafts, sunk on the Polgear lodes, would be used to drain the adjacent china-clay land. A deposit of excellent peat, in some places seven or eight feet deep, extended over much of the surface, and as soon as the other operations were a little advanced it was proposed to start making peat charcoal, of which it was estimated some 5,000 tons a year could be produced at a profit of 30s. per ton.

Unfortunately, the enterprise came to nothing, as the promoters were unable to get possession of the Polgear and Lancarrow mine and machinery, whose operating company was involved in proceedings in the Court of the Vice-Warden of the Stannaries.[85] The intended sites of the workings were probably Mine Field and Shaft Field in Lancarrow, which were only a short distance apart, and in the nearby moor. Many of the old field hedges have since been removed and the land 'improved', and apart from slight surface disturbances there are now no signs of any mining, china-clay or peat workings.

CHAPTER SIX
DUES AND LEASES

DURING THE WORKING of bounds or leased ground the mineral lord was entitled to receive a proportion of the stream-tin or tin-ore raised. The ore took two forms, the tin-gravel raised from stream-workings being washed clean from the waste and in a form ready for the smelter. Ore taken from a lode in an open-work or mine, and poor quality tin-gravel from streams, would be broken small and made fit for stamping and subsequent dressing to bring it into a state suitable for smelting. The mineral lord's share of both of these was known as toll-tin, and was loosely referred to as dues or royalties. With the exception of a few local variants not recorded for Wendron, in Cornwall the mineral lord's share was, by custom, 1-15th of the ore. When the bound-owners leased their bounds to a third party they reserved a proportion of the ore remaining after the toll-tin had been taken out. This proportion varied from one part of the county to another, but was generally 1-10th and was known as farm tin. However, if pitches in the bounds were let on tribute to individual parties of tinners, the tribute payable might be as much as a third or a quarter of the ore remaining after the toll-tin had been taken out. Thus a party of tributers taking a pitch on bounds at one-third tribute would keep about 62 per cent. of the black tin they raised, though tinners who took the whole bounds and paid a farm of one-tenth would keep some 84 per cent. The varying rates of tribute reflected the difference between poor and rich ground, and between easily-worked tin gravels and the more difficult workings on the backs of lodes. If leased ground, or part of it, was already bounded, the bound-owner would claim farm tin from the lessees. In 1840 Frederick Hill, the Helston solicitor, stated that in Wendron it was the custom to divide the dues equally between the bounder and the landlord, though at the time of writing no documentary evidence of this custom has been found.

When in a state fit for smelting or stamping the ore was divided into heaps or doles (shares). The mineral lord took his one-fifteenth, after which each person entitled to a share took what was his or hers. No money changed hands until the ore was sold to a smelter (who paid in bills) or bargain-buyer.

The practice of paying toll-tin or dues in kind fell into disuse in the eighteen-thirties, when a Court ruled that if dues were paid in cash the mineral workings were not assessable to the poor rate. A lessee of the toll-tin or dues was, however, liable to pay rates on tin-works even though he did not live in the parish.[86] Some of the last tin dues to be paid in kind in Cornwall came from Wendron in 1837, when $5\frac{1}{2}$ tons of black tin were sold as 'Wheal Ann dues', and realised £285.12s.6d. In drawing mining leases in the eighteen-fifties it became the custom to describe the dues as rent, with a view to avoiding payment of the poor rate.[87]

Before a piece of land could be prospected or worked for tin it would have been bounded if in unenclosed land or leased if in enclosed land, as we have already seen. A few early leases of mining ground in Wendron have survived. Of these the oldest yet seen is dated November 1574 and gives a good example of the methods employed by mineral lords four centuries ago to ensure that their lands were properly worked. It shows that Henry Donston, gentleman, of Tregaddra, Mawgan in Meneage, was the mineral lord of land in Porkellis. Acting for himself and for John Oppy, Richard Trethowyn (who had died during the negotiations for the lease), and his widow Wilmott Trethowyn, he granted for five years to John Thomas, gentleman, of Constantine, the right to 'set and let' in 'all the severall parte partes porcions and rights in Porthkillis'. This included surface and underground deposits of tin both in the several and in the wastrel, as well as the slimes and wastes from former workings. Dues on ore raised in the Porkellis wastrel were 1-15th and were to be settled in ore, a rate and practice which continued for another two and a half centuries. In the 'farme groundes', or bounded land, dues were 1-10th of the ore, while 1-6th of the remainder was payable to the bounders, whom, one suspects, were Donston and his three companions.

The ground thus leased excluded 'certyn olde water workes', or tin-streams, already taken by John Thomas under a separate deed. It included The Redde Worke, on and adjoining Porkellis Moor and lying west of Hagarowell Lane (called Halwin Lane on modern maps) and an adjoining property on the hillside above it called Parke an Banall (the broom field), at 1-7th dues. Henry Donston may have been the sole mineral lord of this part, since he alone reserved the right to have one man in twelve working there. Another property included in the deed was 'an olde water worke called Hagarowall and all that worke that goythe uppe to the hilwardes by the hedge of that close', which probably lay

west of Hagarowell Lane. Lastly came The Blewe Worke, possibly on the Blue lode, later Wheal Cock lode of Basset and Grylls Mine, set at 1-8th dues for the first year and 1-7th for each subsequent year. It might have been a new working which still required a certain amount of development before it came into full production. For his part Thomas undertook to pay for 'the workes going to the hill begyneninge (sic) at Bosharthye shafte' at the same rate, with Donston having the right to place one man in the workings.

The deed contained several covenants regarding the way in which the properties were to be opened up. Thomas undertook, for instance, to bring up an audit (adit, but still pronounced oddit in the district) or tye to The Redde Worke, and to use his uttermost efforts to bring an audit or tye to Hagarowell and also to maintain and continue it at his pleasure if profits permitted. He was also bound to have his tin ore dressed at Donston's stamping-mill at Trelubbas Wollas, some three miles away, and to deliver sufficient ore there to keep the mill supplied. He was allowed to have any surplus over and above this stamped elsewhere, but all the caselties (casualties) from the ore, wherever dressed, had to be brought back to Donston's lands. Furthermore, Thomas had to fill in all trial pits and shafts that were unprofitable to the mineral lords. Donston reserved the right to have one man working with any new company formed to work the tin on his lands, paying such fearme (farm) to the bounders as Thomas paid to him. A separate clause stipulated that during the five years of the lease Thomas was to give Donston at least twelve hours' notice of washes of tin.

Thomas also covenanted to lend Donston by 12 January 1575 £20 in money or in white coined tin, valued at the Michaelmas (29 September) coinage price of £21 per thousandweight (1,000 lbs). A further 1,000 lbs of white tin was to be lent to Donston at the Michaelmas 1575 coinage at the best price that should then be set. Donston agreed to repay these sums by the Feast of St James the Apostle (25 July)

1576, in the equivalent of black tin made good, clean and merchantable. This Thomas was allowed to take in instalments out of the black tin to which Donston was entitled as mineral lord. The price at which the black tin was to be taken in settlement of the loans was 'ijd. ob. the m:ke', or 2¹/₂d. per mark, a measure of about eight ounces.[88] In this ingenious fashion Thomas was encouraged to get the property into production as soon as he could, since the repayment of his loans was directly dependent on the output of black tin. Within a few years 'Port Kellis' was one of the largest tin-works in the district.[89]

Next comes a lease from 1627 which covered Porkellis Wollas (Lower Porkellis), and which included part of the low-lying land on either side of the road running southwards from that hamlet. Lacking the names of the lessees, it was of a kind intended to be read out annually to the takers of pitches. It recited that Samuel Pendarves of Roskrow, William Pendarves of Skewis, and Thomas Flamank (as heir of Rise) leased the property for one year. One of the conditions was that every tinner should only work such ground as should be allotted to him, and another was that he should pay 1-5th part of all the tin-ore he raised to the three lessors. Half the ore raised was to be stamped at the stamps of Samuel and William Pendarves, and the other half at those of Flamank.[90] After allowing for the 1-15th of the ore claimed by the mineral lord, the tinners would have kept a little less than three-quarters of the ore they raised.

Carew's description of balls as 'the Vales where the works are set on foote' could well have been inspired by Porkellis Moor, for in the eighteenth century, two centuries after he wrote, the area was still divided into 'balls' or groups of workings. Above Porkellis Bridge, on and east of the river Cober, in unenclosed land, lay Porkellis Ball, which included both stream-works and underground workings. Adjoining it to the south were numerous small underground workings such as Wheals Tallack and Vernon, which in 1789 formed part of Wheal Enys, named after the mineral lord. Below the bridge lay Mean Vrose, variously spelt, which was also known as Wheal an Grease (the middle work) or Wheal Grease Ball, or as The Middle Ball. Lower down the Moor and adjacent to it lay the area described in old deeds as Porkellis Moor. Still further downstream the part of the Moor extending to Trenear was known as Trenear Moor. On the slopes of the valley of the Carnkie branch of the river Cober lay Ball Reeth, formerly The Redde Worke, roughly south-west of Lower Porkellis, while on the south side of the stream lay Garlidna Ball. There were no exact lines of division between the balls, though the boundary of Garlidna Ball and Ball Reeth may have followed the boundary of the mineral ownership.[91]

Part of Wheal an Grease Ball was bounded about 1749 by and for the use of John Hughes, Reginald Bawden, Edward Hodge and Warwick Oben. In that year they set six pitches , each taker agreeing to employ a specific number of men. The takers were Samuel Dowa, John Pascoe alias Burgon, William Gundry alias Punch, Martin Pascoe, Richard Carn and John Thomas. All but Gundry and Carn were illiterate, and all made their mark or signed the deed. Only part of the bounded area was set, and John Hughes and his colleagues retained the right to drive levels north and south of the pitches, which were on three east-west lodes crossing the Moor. The takers undertook to remove the gravel and rubbish falling into the dams or catch-pits once in every twelve hours. They also undertook to pay tribute (or farm) to the setters after the lord's dues had been deducted, such payments to be settled in ore. Three pitches were on Mundic lode at a tribute of one-quarter, and there was one pitch each on William Bolitho's lode, Wheal Wearne lode, and on the branches between Wheal Crago lode and William Bolitho's lode, all at a tribute of one-third. In addition to the tribute, the takers were bound to leave one-sixth of all ore remaining after the lord's dues had been settled, as security to the setters; and on the westernmost pitch, which lay between the engine-leat and 'the clay', the taker was forbidden to cut into or through the clay.[92]

In 1751 a lease of Porkellis Moor was granted by Mr Basset of Tehidy to William Sandys, at 1-9th dues. The terms were somewhat complicated, and the deed is of particular interest since it shows that underground miners' interests and those of the mineral lord over-rode those of the surface worker. There was, for instance, a proviso allowing Mr Basset to work any ground left unworked after notice to work it had been served on the lessee, but such ground was not to be on the run of any known lode or within ten fathoms of an adit being driven. Sandys had to erect a water-wheel to work the mine effectually unless hindered by water or other unavoidable impediment, and to give the lessor six days' notice of any division of ore between the parties entitled to a share. The lease covered an area south and south-west of Porkellis village, containing as much of Ball Reeth adit as lay within the premises of Porkellis in the possession of William Pryn and Anthony Pryor, and throughout the old work called Ball Reeth and Thomas Bolitho's Garden, as well as so much of the town place of Porkellis as belonged to Mr Basset. The lessees for their part had liberty to take up adits and to bring waters in and through their mine, and also through Tellam's

Three Moors and such others of Anthony Pryor's premises as belonged to Tymorgy Mine and was so marked and bounded.[93]

In the eighteen-twenties the Ball Reeth part of the property was leased to the Wheal Foster company, together with Wheal Ruby and Garlidna.[94] Wheal Foster and Tymorgy later formed the southern part of Basset and Grylls mine, of which the Ball Reeth adit became the main adit. The lobby of this adit can still be seen, and drinking water is pumped from one of the adit shafts, since it is thought to be much nicer than 'that company stuff' from the mains.

In the nineteenth century, in addition to part of the Manor of Polgear, Lancarrow Moor may also have been leased, since from 1837 the dues collected from it were reduced from 1-15th to 1-20th. It may, in fact, have been the un-named working referred to by Henwood, in which the dues were less than usual because the difficulty and risk were exceptionally great. Here it might be observed that leases of ground for tin-streaming, based on the numbers employed and involving periodical payments similar to rent, as noted by Pryce, have not been recorded for Wendron and are not commented on by later writers.[95]

CHAPTER SEVEN
EDWARD SMITH AND CAPTAIN CREASE

SINCE THE MIDDLE Ages the Duchy of Cornwall has owned the rights to the minerals in Duchy manors. For many years, instead of collecting dues on the minerals being worked, it leased them for a fixed sum, and as early as 1509 John Skewys is known to have leased the dues on tin in the Manor of Helston in Kerrier, which covered about half the parish of Wendron. In 1761, in accordance with its long-established practice, the Duchy farmed its dues to Nicholas Donnithorne, and in 1797 to the Trustees of Isaac Donnithorne, the administrator of Nicholas Donnithorne, in consideration of the surrender of the earlier lease.[96] In August 1810 Edward Smith, of Ince Castle, near Saltash, bought the lease of the dues for £18,500. Of this sum, £11,492 was in consideration of surrendering the old lease, and £6,558 was paid to the Duchy for the new one. On the completion of the documentary formalities Edward Smith put notices in the Cornish papers stating that he held the rights to tin dues under H.R.H. the Duke of Cornwall, and cautioned those whom it might concern against attempts by others to grant leases in his name. He added that any such leases were only valid if they bore his signature and seal of office. This warning he repeated in the press in 1813, 1818 and 1819. It is clear that some confusion had arisen by virtue of the fact that some of the leases granted by the Donnithorne trustees still had some years to run when the Duchy lease changed hands, and that Smith was entitled to the dues on them. In 1813 he advertised a list of his mineral agents, including Walter Harris of Porkellis, and in the spring of 1814 he advertised that he would be passing through Cornwall, calling at St Austell, Truro and Helston, with a view to granting leases in Duchy land. Leases for mines that had been unworked for a year and a day would be considered void; and he intended to seize bounds improperly worked.[97]

Having acquired a new lease, Edward Smith advertised in October 1815 from Plymouth Dock (now Devonport) that he was forming a great company called the Royal Cornish Tin Mining and Smelting Company, in ten shares, of which he would retain one and sell nine. He himself would supply the assets of the company, which would be his interests in tin dues in the Duchy manors, a 1-8th share in the dues on copper in the Manor of Tywarnhayle (St Agnes), and a 1-16th share in copper dues in several other Duchy manors of which he was negotiating the purchase. The dues received from the mines and openworks leased by Smith would be used to pay dividends on the shares. Once again he stressed that since he acquired his interests in the Duchy minerals he had not granted any leases of mines; and it appeared that there were no legal bounds over stream-works on Duchy land.[98] The latter presumably included bounds in the Wendron district, shares in some of which were being offered for sale. The flotation of the proposed company, the first and only one of its kind, was, however, a failure, so Edward Smith proceeded to grant leases of bounds and mines on his own account.

At this point Henry Crease comes into the picture, since he married Edward Smith's daughter Mary. A naval lieutenant, he had distinguished himself while commanding one of two divisions of a raiding party from the frigate Menelaus on the shores of Chesapeake Bay in August 1814. He achieved the rank of Commander in 1821 but saw no service after that date, and was on half pay for many years while enjoying the courtesy title of Captain.[99] About 1827 he began to act for his father-in-law in mining matters, and in 1838, on Edward Smith's death, he bought for 18,500 guineas, at an auction which attracted 'spirited competition', 'the Lease of the Toll and Farm of Tin and Tin Mines' (to give the Duchy rights their full title), from his estate. This permitted him to collect the dues which had formerly been collected by Edward Smith. The head-lease of the dues was for 99 years or three lives from 1815, at an annual rent of £38, while Crease's lease was from his father-in-law's executors and was for 21 years.[100] The lease was determined before it expired, however, and the Duchy resumed control of its mineral rights in the mid-1840s at the instigation of HRH Prince Albert, who was Lord Warden of the Stannaries from 1842 until his death in 1861. Meanwhile, in his capacity of Edward Smith's agent, Captain William Penprase of Grampound gave notice in the summer of 1830 that neither he nor any other agent of the Duchy lessee had any right to refuse a tin sett to an efficient company of adventurers, even if they refused to allow such agent to become an adventurer in the concern. His instructions were to give the tinners every encouragement.[101]

Captain Crease, who held the lease of the Duchy tin jointly with his wife, turned to his new acquisition with a will, and continued to press Edward Smith's claim that the Duchy

lease authorised him to grant leases. In the summer of 1832 he sued one Read for dues on tin taken from an un-named mine in the Manor of Helston in Kerrier. Later in the year his solicitors advertised that the Creases would enforce their rights in Court to the 1-15th share from bounders. In 1833 he published a four-page pamphlet addressed to the Tinners of Cornwall, in which he recited his claim to the 1-15th toll or farm of tin and the right to lease tin mines in enclosed lands. In 1834 he advertised that if persons were deterred from working for tin in the Manor of Helston in Kerrier they should get in touch with his Truro solicitor, George Gillson, who would show that Captain Crease had a good title to the Duchy minerals. Two years later he had some correspondence with the Duchy, which claimed that he had no power to grant setts in wastrel, and in 1837 we find him writing to the Duchy from a West End address to ask for a breakdown of the Duchy dues of £9,818.0s.3d. collected the previous year.[102]

Captain Crease lived in Flushing in 1831 and in Penryn from 1835 to 1842. In 1843 he had an account at the Western District Bank in Falmouth, as well as another in Plymouth, and possibly one in London also. In 1856 he was living at 16 Athenaeum Street, in one of the most prosperous parts of Plymouth, and died there at the end of 1862. Some of his enthusiasm for mining was inherited by his sons Henry Pering Pellew Crease (whose third Christian name was that of the Captain who had been his father's first commander), and Edward V. Crease, who, with their father, were principals in the reopening of Wheal Vor in Breage in 1852.[103]

When Captain Crease began looking after Edward Smith's tin interests in 1827 he employed Captain William Penprase to collect dues at a commission of 2s. in the £. In 1833 the two men made up their mutual accounts, though in the following year, after his dismissal from the post of toller, Captain Penprase continued to collect Captain Crease's dues. As he did not account for them the latter took him to Court, which ruled that in the case of mutual accounts between a lessee of dues and his toller it would restrain proceedings at law, and would direct that the whole accounts be taken in equity, the Master being as good a judge as a jury in such matters. What happened afterwards is not clear; but a Captain Penprase was manager of the lead-smelting works on Tregothnan Consols mine in Kea in 1835. In that year Captain Crease dismissed William Hoskins, his toller for the Manor of Tywarnhayle, who in 1846 claimed rights to bounds in the Scorrier area as a 'privileged tinner'.[104]

Meanwhile, in 1835 Captain Crease (of whom it had been said that he was an honourable member of an honourable profession and that he 'had never failed in any trial at Law') took a bounder named Barrett to Court for the non-payment of dues, in the shape of black tin. The case arose in the Duchy Manor of Tewington, near St Austell, and the Court ruled that it was part of the custom of bounding for the tinner claiming under it to pay a certain toll to the owner of the minerals, which in that Manor was a customary 1-10th. Following the successful outcome of the case Captain Crease advertised in the *Mining Journal* in May 1836 that anyone taking a lease from a tin bounder in Duchy land, and agreeing to pay dues to such bounder, would still be compelled to pay Captain Crease the full customary toll, which varied in the Duchy manors between 1-15th and 1-6th. After detailing his reasons for this Captain Crease reminded his readers that the county at large had benefited from the proceedings he had taken for exposing the fraudulent nature of the bound claim monopoly, for if he had not opposed these claims many of the mines then working would be idle. He had also opposed the claims by the gentlemen of Helston to 1-9th of the black tin raised by streamers, for the use of waters, and concluded by stating that smelters were not liable to account for dues to the mineral lord or bounders.[105]

About this time, on the application of James Plomer, a Helston solicitor acting for Messrs. Hill and others, the Vice-Chancellor ordered Bennet Johns to be committed to the Fleet Prison, together with several miners who had helped him to fill a shaft near White Alice in land Captain Crease had leased to the adventurers in Balmynheer mine. On hearing affidavits in reply, supporting Captain Crease's right to the spot in question, the Vice-Chancellor discharged the order, and awarded costs against the applicant parties. In June 1837 Bennet Johns, a farmer, of Bodilly, and Overseer of the Poor for Wendron since 1828, was appointed by Captain Crease as his toller or collector of dues for the Manor of Helston in Kerrier, an appointment which lasted until October 1845. It is thanks to the discovery of the notebook in which Johns recorded his receipts and payments that it is possible to form a picture of the tin-streaming and mining that went on in Duchy land in Wendron during that time. The office of collector subsequently passed first to his son Bennet Johns junior and then to his grandson Bennet Rogers Johns, the last of the Duchy collectors for the area.[106]

The properties on whose produce Johns collected dues fell into three categories. Numerically the most important were the tin-streams and openworks, the latter sometimes known as stennacks (though this term was also applied to streams) and as hownans, probably from the Cornish haun, a ravine, and nans, a valley.[107] These paid dues in cash on their sales of black tin, at the customary rate of 1-15th except where they were the subject of a lease or of special arrangements. The second category, and the most important financially, comprised the underground or deep mines, which were leased at 1-18th or 1-20th dues. Thirdly came the dumps and waste on the surface of abandoned mines, which were worked by tributers, usually at 1-15th dues but on one occasion at a rate of 1-5th, or 4s. in the £, a reflection both on the dressing methods employed at the defunct Balmynheer mine and on the hope of a relatively easy task in working the waste, a hope that was not fulfilled. No payments were recorded specifically as such by streamers working the waste from stamping-mills; and several of the mines paid dues direct to Captain Crease. The smallness and infrequency of many of the payments show that, apart from Porkellis Moor, the area had already seen the best of its tin-streaming days, and that much of the working was likely to have been seasonal.

In noting payments received Johns gives the date, the name and address of the payer, the location of the working, the rate of dues, and the amount paid. The location was generally a moor or moors, then the local name for any place where tin was streamed. If the working was in enclosed land, its name and the name of the estate in which it lay were given. It is probable that most of the stream-workings in unenclosed lands were very small concerns, which, as noted by Carew two and a half centuries earlier, did not have a name. Payers' addresses were essential to avoid confusion, since there might well have been several people of the same name in the parish. Quite a number of families were engaged in tin-streaming at the time, notably the Bolithos, the Combellacks, the Jenkins, the Moyles, the Perrys, the Pryors and the Tresidders, names still known in the district today, and some of whom had several streams working at a time and some of whom must occasionally have moved house. In some places there was more than one stream; and as Johns wrote phonetically he has unwittingly recorded the contemporary pronunciations of such places as Carnebonellis, Fiscor, Puligy and Yalow Work, now Carnmenellis, Viscar, Polhigey and Yellow Wort.[108]

The calculation of dues on mine-tin was done by the mine's purser. That on stream tin was a simple matter, since all Johns had to do was to work out a fifteenth of the net sum shown on the smelter's bill. Sometimes the streamer forgot to bring the bill with him, for there are several entries of 'the Bill not Perdussed', indicating that the payment might be an estimate of the amount due. A total of 301 payments is recorded during the eight years and five months that Johns kept the record, an average of about three payments a month. The busiest months for collecting were December and January, and the slackest were March, June and October, when tin-streamers were working on farms. Many, in fact, were smallholders or farmers. No dues were collected at all in June and July 1838. Johns received 2s. in the £ as his commission on the sums he collected, plus occasional gifts from Captain Crease. The sums varied between £40.8s.3d. from Wheal Ruby mine and one and fourpence from a working on the nearby Halwin stream. A list of streamers paying dues at this time is given in Appendix B.

Bennet Johns made up his accounts for Captain Crease at irregular intervals, and the first one, exceptionally, only covers the five months from June to October 1837, evidently so that Captain Crease could satisfy himself that Johns fully understood his duties. During this period only £2.16s.11½d. was collected, out of which Johns received a 1s. fee and a present of 1s. When Captain Crease had checked this and subsequent accounts he signed them as 'seen and allowed' or as 'Settled'. After the deduction of Johns' fees, and of poor, road and church rates, the balance was paid to Captain Crease, or to his bank, or to other parties to his order. Income tax was charged half-yearly from 1842 at 7d. in the £ on an assumed annual income of £200, of which the first £150 was not taxable.[109] Over the period covered by the book a total of £1,318.5s.11d. was paid by the streamers and miners in dues, of which Johns collected £772.10s.8d. personally, the rest being paid direct to Captain Crease by the pursers of Wheal Ann, Crahan Mine, and Wheal Trumpet. Of the total sum £331.5s.10d. or 20 per cent. came from streams and openworks, £19.16s. or one per cent. from dumps, and £967.4s.1d. or 79 per cent. from mines. Commissions and presents paid to Johns amounted to £103.19s.10d., while £53.17s.10d. went in poor, road and church rates, £4.7s.6d. in income tax and £99.1s.5d. in miscellaneous expenses, as follows:

1840	Gweek Company bill, timber for Balcoath and Wheal Jane mine	£11.15.0
	Bennet Johns, carriage of 175 ft. of timber to above	£0.12.10
	Joseph Read, securing windows at Balmynheer Mine (on abandonment of account-house)	£0.6.0
1842-43	Calls on Captain Crease's shares in West Wheal Lovell mine	£13.6.0
	Labour and expenses, Treloar and Crowgey mine	£58.16.7
1843-44	Legal expenses: Hartley £5.17s.6d.; Penprase 14s.6d.; Teague 4s.	£6.16.0
1844	John Trembath, wages on account, and Richard Gilbert, horse hire	£3.14.6
	James Kempthorne, expenses to London	£2.15.0
	Bennet Johns, half expenses to Plymouth	£0.19.6
		£99.1.5

It is not possible to calculate with any great accuracy the amount of black tin sold during the period, since the price varied from day to day and from parcel to parcel, each of which was sold by assay, and as the official average metal, prices were only estimated annually and then only to the nearest £ per ton. However, the figures indicate an average metal price of £80.4s.5d. per ton between 1837 and 1845, and, if one assumes the average grade of black tin to have been 65 per cent. metal and takes 65-100ths of the metal price as being the black tin price, this would give the latter an average price of £52.2s.3d. per ton. Taking the dues on mines at 1-20th, but on Wheal Ruby at the published 1-18th and on stream-works and dumps at 1-15th, the £1,318.5s.11d. received in dues by Captain Crease would turn would represent very roughly 457 tons of black tin, or about one-third of the 1,552 tons sold by Geevor mine in the year to end-March 1986, the last year for which normal figures are available.[110] In modern times, with tin metal at its current depressed price of $4,385 per tonne and sterling at $1,517, 457 long tons of black tin (65 per cent. metal) would be worth some £858,650.

In January 1841 Cornwall Great United Mines, one of the early holding companies, relinquished its leases of Treloar and Crowgey, two farms on which a tin-stream was situated, and which it had only held for six years. The company retained Laity, site of another tin-stream, on which it sank a shaft. Treloar and Crowgey Moors were streamed for tin in 1841 by Daniel Wearne of Carnebone, while Captain Crease was forming a company to work them as West Wheal Lovell. It was also referred to as Western Sett Wheal Lovell, perhaps owing to its close connection with Wheal Lovell, then managed by Mrs Lydia Taylor, Cornwall's only lady mine manager.[111]

In 1842 there were complications over a license which Captain Crease had granted to three tin-streamers named Jenkins, Moyle and Crocker, who were charged with an alleged trespass on lands in the Manor (estate) of Polgear. The lands in question were held by a receiver under a Court order of 1831 as their lessee, Mrs Mary Hartley, of Higher Trelill, Wendron, was of unsound mind. Her receiver claimed a title to a life-interest in the disputed lands in a term of seven years, renewable for ever without fine (the normal terms for a Duchy lease), while the defendants claimed a title to the minerals under the land. Evidently Vice-Chancellor Shadwell was in some doubt as to the local customs, since he ruled that although the minerals had been reserved by the mineral lord the license did not give the right to enter on the lands in question and to work the minerals, and ordered that the rights of all parties be determined.[112] This was evidently done fairly quickly, and was settled in the streamers' favour. Bennet Johns recorded the receipt of dues of 1-15th from William Crocker of Lancarrow on the working of Polgear Moors in May 1842, October 1843 and July 1845, and dues at the same rate, later reduced to 1-20th, on the produce of Lancarrow Moor, at fairly regular intervals between 1837 and 1845, so it is not possible to state whether or for how long the lawsuit interrupted the workings. Johns' charge of £5.17s.6d.

'Expense with Evidences in the Sute of Mrs Hartley.' would have covered the cost of a trip to London to attend the Court hearing.

Pages from Bennet Johns' notebook. *Justin Brooke*

CHAPTER EIGHT
DECLINE

IN 1819 THE stream-works in Wendron were productive, and were said to repay the labourers amply. About the middle of the century there were some twenty pares or companies of streamers at work in Porkellis Moor. According to the late J. T. Rapson of Boderluggan these early streamers wore 'woolen overhauls', and the man who stood in the water in the buddle wore thick-bottomed boots and leather up to the knees, called broogs. At one time there were two parties of streamers in the Moor, known as the Mamalukes and the Pirates, who competed with each other in times of drought for the little water available, cutting down and building up the water-courses, 'but as soon as the Season changed they would again work in peace and harmony', according to local tradition. They used to eat their dinners (south-western for lunches) in little houses or huts, and sing their songs, 'and sometimes offer their prayers and praises, and my Father has told me of the valley ringing with the praise to the God of Heaven'. [113]

The decline of tin-streaming in the Wendron moors took place in the second half of the nineteenth century, at a time when underground mining was expanding. As far as Porkellis and Trenear Moors were concerned this expansion was, paradoxically, in part assisted by the streamers themselves, who in the course of their operations over the years discovered and worked the backs of lodes as far as the water would permit. They did not benefit in 1850 from the formation of the mining companies called Porkellis United and Wendron Consols, since they lacked both the capital and the expertise needed to run a mine and to work their lodes on a large scale and in depth. Their only reward, if reward it can be called, seems to have been the naming after some of their number of Moyle's lode (two), Richards' lode, and Gluyas' shaft, and their subsequent employment on tribute as tin-dressers, working the leavings at the stamping-mills. The frustration the streamers felt on being turned away in favour of a mining company is remembered in the district to this day. [114]

An illustration of the progress of underground mining in Wendron is shown by the number of steam-engines at work. In 1846 there were only six of all kinds in the parish, of which two were at Wheal Ruby and Garlidna (70-inch and 58-inch cylinder), and one each at Medlyn Mines (30-inch), Wheal Ann (48-inch), and Wheal Lovell (50-inch). Eleven years later there were nine pumping-engines, the largest being a 70-inch at Wendron Consols and a 60-inch at Basset and Grylls, the new name for Porkellis United. By 1862 there were seventeen mines at work, employing 1,860 people and using 28 steam-engines for pumping, hauling and stamping. [115]

Dressing the low-grade waste from mines was the last and riskiest operation in tin-dressing, at least from the point of view of the mining companies, since time could be wasted in attempting to dress unpayable material. In 1828 it was sometimes the practice of mining companies to let the tin-dresser dress the leavings on his own account, at a certain proportion of the value of the crop or richest tin, and restricting the dressing of the crop tin to the buddle, kieve and sieve.[116] Nearly thirty years later, dressing the waste at Wendron Consols mine, at the lower end of the moor above Trenear, was carried out on tribute. The mine's books show that there were various kinds of low-grade material to be dressed, and that they came under the general heading of leavings. They included halvans, whits, slimes, tails or tailings, leavings and after-leavings. The mine leased Sithney Coverack Stamps, where the leavings were set to Samuel Rogers in October 1857. They extended so far west as the dressing-frame shed, and so far south as the catch-pit. Rogers agreed to employ not less than five able persons and to provide all the materials except frames and hand-barrows. He was obliged to sample the black tin he recovered as often as the agents of the mine directed, to pay the smelters' returning charges according to the rules of the mine, and to forfeit for every breach of duty or neglect as the agents should fix. The contract ran for four months, and Rogers received 10s. in the £ on the value of the black tin he recovered. At the same stamps John Jeffery took all the after-leavings, or what was left of the leavings after Rogers and his party had dressed them, and which extended 20 fathoms west of the mill leat. He worked them on his own for a month and kept 15s. in the £ worth of black tin he recovered.

'All the leavings that was given up at Trelubbas stamps by John Williams', extending so far east, west, north and south as marked out by boundary pins, were set in November 1857 to William Teague. He had to provide all his own materials except trams and hand-barrows, and was obliged to sample when instructed. His remuneration was 10s. in the £ on the black tin recovered, based on a notional price of £60 per ton;

the previous week's price for first-quality black tin was £59.10s. to £62.10s. per ton. The halvans and slimes at Trenear Stamps, the main dressing-floors of Wendron Consols, were similarly set in February 1858 to Peter Moyle at 8s.9d. in the £ for one month. In May 1858 the contract was renewed for four months at 7s.6d. in the £, a rate renewed for three months in January 1860 and for another quarter in April, this time 'to dress by a sufficient pare of Boys and Girls and keep away the stuff for the Quarter ending June 1860.' The Sampling-book shows that Moyle continued to work the halvans until January 1865, while Andrew Adams worked the Trelubbas whits from October 1861 to June 1864. Meanwhile, in June 1860, Bennett Moyle & Co., a three-man pare consisting of Bennett Moyle, Edward Moyle and Bennett Moyle junior, took a month's contract, 'the halvans to wash and burrow to pick and turn over by three men', at 6s.8d. in the £. The following month the same people contracted for a month to work 'all the wast (sic) drawn at Bishop's shaft and the burrow to wash and pick by three men' at the same rate. [117]

During the working of the waste from stamping-mills several devices were adopted for dressing the fine slimes. Notable among these was the Cornish rag-frame (a corruption of rack-frame), which was already in use in the 1870s. Several of these were in use at Coverack Stamps in the 1920s and on the Red River in Camborne thirty years later. An improvement on the frame described by Pryce,[118] but a trifle inefficient when very low-grade material was being treated, it consisted of a wooden deck some six to eight feet long and three to four feet wide, its upper end being very slightly higher than its lower. Below the lower end, at right-angles to the line of flow, were two launders, one for concentrates and another for tailings. The slimes, in suspension in water, were fed slowly to the top of the frame, and as they flowed towards the bottom the fine black tin settled on the frame and the lighter waste flowed into the tailings launder. While this was going on a vee-launder pivoted across the top of the frame was filling

Dressing Plant, 1920s, Porkellis Moor. *Eric Edmonds*

slowly with fresh water. When full the launder overbalanced, cutting off the feed of slime to the frame, and washing the fine tin which had settled on it down into the concentrate launder via a pivoted flap. In practice it was found that the sudden flow of water only removed part of the black tin, and that some of it went into the tailings launder. This was overcome by dividing the deck into upper and lower parts, and by having two concentrate launders and a second vee-launder above the lower part of the deck. Most of the fine black tin settled on the upper deck, and was washed into a launder at its lower end. The washing cycle lasted only a few minutes ;

and in 1873 it was reckoned that one boy could attend to twenty frames.[119]

The dangers which attended mining near old stream-works were demonstrated in August 1858 at Porkellis United Mines, where an old openwork on the back of a lode was being used as a slimes pond for the adjacent dressing-floors. Between eleven and twelve o' clock one morning the mine workings on Date's lode (formerly called Moyle's) fell in from surface to about the 24 fathom level and, communicating with an old shaft on the same lode, where a sollar gave way, opened up a channel for the slimes in the old openwork. The slimes flowed into the mine with a noise like thunder, and Goatley's, Wheal Ash and some other shafts were filled to near the 24 fathom level. Six men and a boy, who had been working in the shaft and at the ends of the deepest levels, were entombed. The remainder of the fifty-odd men who were underground at the time managed to escape, as did some girls working at the dressing-frames at surface. The ground around the main shaft for some twenty or thirty fathoms subsided about three feet, taking with it about a dozen dressing-frames. In other places it subsided some thirty or forty feet, the total area affected being over a quarter of an acre, and close to the road.[120] According to local tradition the management knew the ground underneath the old streamers' pit was unsafe, and had boarded up the access to the level under it. However, the tributers working in the mine loosened a couple of boards to gain access to a rich deposit of tin there, and unknown to all but themselves they removed ore from it over the years. Finally, the ground was weakened to such an extent that it collapsed.[121]

The accident was the first serious one since the East Wheal Rose, Newlyn East, disaster twelve years earlier, and the *Mining Journal* carried three different accounts of it in the same issue. Great numbers of people from the surrounding districts visited the scene, and a week after the accident the ground was said to be so soft that some of it was still falling

in. The accident closed the mine, for the shareholders were not able or willing to put up the money to reopen it. It also caused the Truro correspondent of the *Mining Journal* (probably Robert Symons, born in Breage) to observe that governments in a South American republic did not succeed each other with more rapidity than the different administrations in Porkellis United, and, as might be expected, with a result not dissimilar. In its short life of eight years the mine had seven managers, a record that stands unbroken to this day. At the time of the accident it was noted that the growan in the mine had the quality of swelling or 'plumming' when exposed to the atmosphere, and to such a degree in some places was this the case that what in one week would be deemed perfectly safe and adequately timbered, in the next might be highly dangerous. This had been particularly noticed at the Wendron Consols mine, south-west of Porkellis United, where ample precautions had been taken.[122]

Not surprisingly, a little folk-lore grew up around tin-streaming down the centuries. Tales of the Phœnicians having come to Cornwall to buy tin go back to the seventeenth century. Other beliefs include 'attall sarazin', mentioned by Carew as meaning 'Jews' offcasts', the waste from early stream-workings allegedly conducted by those people. Although *sarazin* is similar to the Cornish *sarsyn*, a Saracen, Moor, or Moslem, these gentlemen are unlikely to have been buyers of tin outside the markets of the Mediterranean, or to have been tin-streamers. The writer believes that sarazin is a corruption of *sawsen*, the Cornish for an Englishman (or Saxon), which suggests that early tin-streaming was undertaken by people from across the Tamar. But it may be a dialect word whose meaning has been lost.[123] Similarly, as we have seen, the remains of primitive smelting-works were called 'Jews' Houses', though what the Jewish connection with the Cornish tin trade may have been has never been adequately explained. England was the last country in western Europe to be settled by the Jews, who arrived after the Norman conquest. Their descendants, all 16,511 of them, were banished from the country in 1290; and Cromwell permitted the Jews to return in 1650.[124] Jew in Cornish is *yedhow*, and Hebrew is *ebbrow*, and had there been any considerable Jewish activity or influence in tin-streaming or smelting, one might expect to find place-names and stream or bound names containing these words, as one does with *sawsen*, but as yet the writer has found none. The first reference seen to Attal Sarazin Moor in Roche is only from 1835; and there was a While an Attol near Sithney church in 1502. And there was a Whele an Jew, possibly a corruption of Wheal an Dew, God's Work, in St Hilary in 1741.

Worthy also of mention is the tale of the Porkellis geese. In 1821 a company was formed to work Wheal Foster and Porkellis Moor Stream Works, which lay to the south and south-west of Porkellis, and which later formed part of the Basset and Grylls mine. Captain Walter Jeffery was manager. The mine only produced small quantities of black tin and closed a few years later with heavy losses. As a result, in 1857 the large number of geese which were pastured in the moor were known locally as Captain Watt Jeffery's enemies, as they were jokingly said to have eaten up all the tin as fast as the captain produced it. By the end of the century the tale had become somewhat elaborated, and it was noted that it was curious to see the selected tin-gravel thrown up by the streamers arranged in small piles, in each of which were embedded stalks of furze or thorn, to prevent them being swallowed by the geese, of which great numbers pastured in the moor.[125] In a desolate area where landmarks were few, pitfalls common, and the tin-gravels largely worked out, other more plausible explanations of this custom, if ever it existed, will readily spring to mind.

Again, local tradition says that the exceptionally rich lodes of the Basset and Grylls mine in Porkellis Moor were found about 1845 by a streamer named Henry Jenkin. While working them he and his partners were peremptorily ousted by the mineral lords on the grounds that their streamers' license did not extend to underground mining. But most of the lodes in the moor were not very rich, and had been found, named and worked over a century earlier. Between 1847 and 1852 eighteen streamers sold black tin from Wheal an Grease, including Henry Jenkin, who made his last sale in September 1851. Most of the streamers had left the area by then, and only four made sales after that date. Porkellis United Mines began mining in the area in 1850, and it is more likely that all the streamers and not Jenkin alone were refused renewals of their licenses or leases (at 1-20th dues) on the ground that, as later events proved, streaming endangered underground mining. And tales of parties of tinners diverting each others' watercourses could also be a fiction, since such behaviour could well lead the offenders to the Stannary Courts, either at the behest of the aggrieved streamers or of the owner or lessor of the watercourse.[126]

Concurrently with the decline of tin-streaming in Wendron the Red River in Camborne became the location of numerous plants working the waste from the surrounding tin-mines. The first plant was laid down in the late eighteen-fifties by a streamer named Jackson. By 1873 the river was already established as the county's most important tin-streaming area. In the seven and a half miles between its source at Higher Bolenowe and the sea at Gwithian there were twenty-seven plants dressing the waste poured into the river and its tributaries by the Camborne, Pool and Illogan mines, and there was also a plant working the beach sands at Gwithian. Some of the plants were said to be partly owned by the agents of those mines,[127] but be that as it may, it is worth noting that the names of some of the principals involved in those operations can also be found in Wendron three decades earlier, notably those of Dinnis, Gluyas, Harris, Perry and Treloar, and it seems quite likely that a few of the early Red River streamers learned their craft on the streams of Wendron.

In the 1860s it was evident that tin-streaming in the Wendron area had declined, and the outputs of the individual streams became so small that for convenience they were summarised in the official Mineral Statistics. It is thus impossible to say which one was the last to report any results, though among the ones to be named separately were Chenhayle (now Chenhall), which sold 10¾ cwt of black tin for £42.17s.5d. in 1860, Halwin, which in the same year sold 2 tons 7¾ cwt for £163.8s.7d., and South Halwin, which sold 5 tons 56 cwt in 1865 for £298.0s.11d. Polmarth or Wheal Richman sold 2 tons 13½ cwt of black tin for £196.9s.1d. in 1872-73, and miscellaneous sales were recorded for the Duchy Manor of Helston in Kerrier up to 1878. Of these, Moyle's Openwork, situated in the fork between the two main branches of the river Cober which meet on Porkellis Moor, was being worked in 1875, when a local correspondent reported that it was pumped by two water-wheels and that ore was brought up from it in barrows. In 1884 no streams are recorded as having produced any black tin or paid any dues, though there is no doubt that during the next half century there were still a few people who maintained a livelihood in Porkellis Moor by 'this most ancient of Cornish industries', as a mining engineer observed three years later.[128] That both tin-streaming and mining were declining was shown in the *Mining Journal* in June 1891, when it was reported 'on authority' that 'all interest in Porkellis, including stock and block' had recently been disposed of for the paltry sum of 19s.6d., and that the former bal-captain had officiated as the temporary auctioneer. Whether a tin-stream or a mine was involved is a matter for conjecture, since the goods which changed hands may have been the residue of an earlier sale, and much of it could have been scrap iron or timber. Meanwhile, in February 1891, Bennett Moyle of Porkellis died at the age of 73. Formerly a tin-streamer, he had spent the greater part of his working life at Wheal Ruby and other Wendron mines. One writer gave it that he and Captain Ned Moyle were the two old Porkellis men who could discourse on the tin-streamers and the vicissitudes of streaming in the Moor in the days of the 'old men'. As hale and robust as in the days of yore, Captain Edward Moyle of Boswin died in April 1892. His death occurred in the middle of a slump in mining and at a time when Lord Robartes was recruiting unemployed miners to reclaim streamed land at Trewavas Downs, adjoining the south side of Porkellis Moor, an operation which was expected to take some years to complete.[129]

This, however, did not spell the end of streaming in the Porkellis moors. In 1893 there was a stream-work run by Thomas Harry Dunstan at Trenear, and in the years before the first World War there was a stream-work 'near Porkellis' and a license was granted to work Chenhayle,[130] though the one-time glories of 'this great tin district' had been all but forgotten by the present generation. Two men were prospecting in the Moor in 1924, and a tin-stream was set up a year or two later to work the wastes from the newly-erected mill below Polhigey Mine, which closed in 1930.[131]

The streaming traditions lived on for a while, and in the nineteen-twenties there were still a few people living in the district who were able to tell of the customs of long ago. For instance, streams were generally worked by parties of two men and four boys, often members of the same family. The first of May was celebrated by the streamers with much drinking, as it was the beginning of their working year, leases being renewed annually on that day. This appears to be a folk-recollection of the custom prevailing in the seventeen-nineties, recorded in a hearing in the Stannary Court, when it was stated that the usual time or season for working in Porkellis Ball was from the first day of May to the first of November in each year.[132]

CHAPTER NINE
DOWN THE COBER VALLEY

AS NOTED BEFORE, the river Cober flows into the sea from the Loe Pool. In the first half of the eighteenth century the Pool was the intended location of an ingenious scheme to recover tin. Some time after 1720 John Warburton, a Fellow of the Royal Society and Somerset Herald in the College of Arms, obtained a lease of Penrose silver-lead mine to the west of the Pool, as well as of the Pool itself. His interest was not confined to underground mining, however, for he intended to recover black tin brought down from the Wendron moors by the river. To effect this he proposed to employ a 'new Invented Engine', in the shape of a wheel working buckets, placed on a sailing barge. This was calculated to be able to bring up sand and gravel from a depth of nine to thirteen feet at a rate of sixty tons an hour. The sketch shows that as the filled buckets came out of the water they were tipped slightly to prevent spilling and then turned through an angle of ninety degrees and discharged through a hole in one side of the barge and into a hopper. The prospectus stated that vast quantities of tin were to be found on the lake bottom and were continually being washed into it, as had been shown when land floods broke over the Loe Bar, and as much as 30,000 sacks (3,000 tons) of black tin had been 'spewed out'. What success, if any, was achieved by this forerunner of the modern bucket dredge is not known; the prospectus sketch showed no source of motive power to drive the bucket-wheel.[133]

A hundred years or so later, in the eighteen-forties, there were still many streams at work on the Cober, some very productive and some considered to be of very remote antiquity. From Trenear down to the Helston town mill the alluvium was being worked by streamers to a greater or lesser extent, and one of the last in this part, in Newham Moor, on the west bank, was still being worked by a man named Liddicoat in the eighteen-fifties.[134] As late as 1873 traces of the streamers' workings were still visible at short intervals. Between the town mill and the Loe Pool, however, although attempts were made at streaming, it was found that the overburden was so thick as to make it virtually impossible to reach what was traditionally affirmed to be very rich tin ground. An effort was made about 1840 to work the deposits, when a large square timber-lined shaft was sunk through the alluvium. Much of the ground passed through was found to contain leaves and twigs of hazel and alder, and so preserved by the bog water that their natural colours were apparent as the masses were turned up. However, a few days' exposure to the air decomposed the mass into a black viscid mud, which pressed so heavily on the timbered sides of the shaft that it crushed them together. It was thus rendered impossible to

The world's first tin-dredge: Mr Warburton's "New Invented Engine" for the Loe Pool. Re-drawn from the original by courtesy of Reginald Rogers & Son, Helston. *Clive Carter*

drive levels from the bottom of the shaft as had at first been intended. One writer claims that the mine was worked after sinking through about thirty feet of mud and sand, but this seems unlikely. The distorted sides of the excavation, and the reeking mass of black slimy mud presented so melancholy an appearance that the name Wheal Caudle (say 'coddle') was given to the operation,[135] caudle being a local dialect word for a mess.

Despite this disappointment, the Weeth Green, below Helston, was bored in 1847 by James M. Rendel, the eminent civil engineer, possibly the first person ever to make such an attempt. He found the killas bedrock at a depth of 28 feet from the surface. His efforts may have led to the formation of a company in the summer of 1850 to work a property measuring 400 by 500 fathoms, which included the Green and an old silver-lead mine called Wheal Pool. The mine lay just north of the Loe Pool, and the remains of its engine-house still stand close to the road to Lower Nanceloe. Instead of working the mine for silver-lead, however, the company erected machinery near the northern end of the property, and started streaming the Green for tin under the borrowed title of Wheal Pool. The workings were drained by a water-wheel and pumps, and a splendid floor of tin-gravel was discovered. At this point the water-wheel proved to be of insufficient power to drain the workings, and they were abandoned. Less than a year later a fresh company took over the property, backed by two engineers named Loam, one from St Day and the other from Liskeard, and by H. F. Stephens, a professional mine company purser from Wadebridge. The last-named advertised for a 50-inch steam-engine in February 1852, but it seems unlikely that one was obtained since work stopped shortly afterwards. Another company was formed to work the property in 1855, and claimed in its prospectus to have 20,000 square fathoms of stream-tin ground. Apart from spending about £500 on preliminaries and appointing Captain John Webb of St Austell as manager the company did

very little until early in 1858, when work was started on the alluvial deposit and 19$\frac{1}{2}$ cwts. of black tin were sold for £71.5s.3d. Its new manager, Captain Henry Harris, was said at the time to be a self-made man and was regarded as a first-rate tinner for the job, which needed more than ordinary skill. The tin-bearing gravels had to be recovered from beneath the silt and bed of a river, and great care had to be exercised in timbering Wheal Cober shaft. By June 1860 a 20-inch steam-engine was draining the excavations. The mud was found to be 26 feet deep, below which lay 3$\frac{1}{2}$ to 4 feet of tin-ground. The first place opened up was a failure, but in the second, thirty feet square, about half the space was underlain by tin-ground. On this they worked about 50 fathoms, making a total of 65 (square) fathoms, from which some £170 worth of black tin was ultimately raised. This gave the ground a value of about £2.10s. per square fathom. The company paid Mr Rogers of Penrose £70 a year for the use of the adit draining the Loe Pool; operations came to an end later in 1860, in which year black tin sales of 1 ton 1$\frac{1}{2}$ cwts. realised £84.10s.1d. In 1862 and again in 1865 unsuccessful attempts were made to form companies to continue the stream-works and to reopen the silver-lead mine. [136]

In 1870 sales of black tin began to be recorded from the Loe Pool Stream Works, and the following year a number of tin-streams began to sell black tin under the title of Helston Stream Works. These were evidently only small workings, since in March 1872 a correspondent of the *Mining World* reported that extensive works for streaming the tin deposits in the Loe Valley below Helston would shortly commence under the management of John Old. Tin in large quantities was believed to be obtainable in the strata underlying the mud and sand. To facilitate operations it would be necessary to open the old adit, which connected the Loe Pool with the sea, and it was said that permission to do this had been obtained at a moderate rent from Mr J. J. Rogers of Penrose. The high price and future prospects of the tin market was

Buddle and retaining wall, part of the installations of the Helston Valley Tin Co. Ltd., erected before World War 1. *Justin Brooke*

expected to make the enterprise a most remunerative one, and it was noted that the mineral rights belonged to the Duchy, operations being carried out from the eastern side of the valley.[137] At about the same time a deposit of sand brought down by the river to the head of the Loe Pool during the winter was being worked.[138]

The attention of the *Royal Cornwall Gazette* was drawn to these streaming activities in 1877, when the paper recorded that the Cober was being worked from Coverack Bridges to the Loe Pool. Mr Dale, who had been a streamer for fifty years, was working (at an unspecified place), as well as several parties at Lower Town, producing from a few hundredweights to as many tons of black tin a month. The machinery was not on such a gigantic scale as that on the Red River in Camborne, yet the streamers on the Cober knew what machinery was best adapted to their work as well as those in other places. It was, the paper observed, surprising that the owners of the Loe Pool, Messrs. Gundry and

Stephens, should not display more activity to work the Pool, where there were only two pulverizers and a few frames at work. The river or lode (deposit) was a full 20 feet wide and a mile and a half long, and the tin-ground, apparently at no great depth, was consequently inexpensive to work. Other streamers at work in the district included William Bishop at Lezerea, James Mitchell at Lower Green, Helston, and James Piper at Halwin.[139]

Stamps foundations near Castle Wary, erected by the Helston Valley Tin Co. Ltd., before World War 1. *Justin Brooke*

There were occasional changes in the management of the Loe Pool works. In 1877 they were leased by Samuel Stephens of Godolphin Bridge, Breage, and in 1880 by William Roberts. In 1880-81 John Stephens and S. H. Stephens & Co. had three streams under the one title, all engaged in treating sand and slime left from mine workings. The streams probably included the stamps at Coverack Bridges and Trelubbas, since the activities of the company included working the wastes from the nearby Trumpet Consols mine and probably other mines as well.[140] In 1882

Captain Samuel H. Stephens was the manager of the stream-works at the Loe Pool, where he had installed a 'much-abused little pulverizer', in use on other tin-streams as well, and for which he as inventor had received a bronze medal from the Royal Cornwall Polytechnic Society. To house the pulverizer and the dressing machinery a dressing-house about 40 feet long had just been built; but the deposit being worked was flooded during the winter.[141] In 1870-78 sales of black tin amounted to 65 tons 4¼ cwts. and realised £3,040.7s.6d. Meanwhile, Helston Stream Works, under which title a number of stream-works were included, began selling black tin in 1871. Over the next seven years, under various similar titles, a total of 51 tons 4¼ cwts. of black tin was sold for £3,172.18s.10d.[142] In 1893 John Pryor owned and may have worked the Lowertown Stream-Works, close to which William Roberts of Sithney held Trenethick Stream Works and John Williams had the Gwealhellis Tin Stream.[143]

Modern methods arrived in the summer of 1912, when boring operations were carried out between Helston and the Loe Pool by a 'well-known' company not mentioned by name. It probably used Banka drills, which had been introduced to Cornwall two years earlier.[144] To work the deposits the Merton Metallurgical Co. Ltd. of London formed a subsidiary called the Helston Valley Tin Co. Ltd., registered at the end of the year and the first limited company to work a tin-stream in the district. The Cornwall correspondent of the *Mining Journal* reported in February 1913 that he had been informed that boreholes put down to discover the depth of payable dirt, before reaching the bedrock, had passed through an average depth of 25 feet of silt, which had evidently come from the Wendron and neighbouring mines. It lay on about 7 feet of sea sand, which in turn lay on 20 to 30 feet of peat. Directly between the peat and the bedrock lay from 4 to 8 feet of alluvial, rich in tin. The writer was assured that the alluvial contained twice as much tin as the silt, although probably only the latter would be worked, and gave

values which would make handsome profits for the proprietors. Although the sand and peat should perhaps have been measured in inches rather than in feet, the presence of sea sand indicates that the trials were made not far upstream from the then head of the Loe Pool.

In June 1913 the Helston Valley company obtained a 31-year lease from the Duchy at 1-20th dues, and under the management first of Richard Hall and then of M. S. Stuchbury proceeded to lay out a dressing-plant at Castle Wary, some eighty feet above the water-level of the recently-constructed ornamental lake at Helston and about half a mile from the town. The tin-bearing silt was first pumped into concrete storage-tanks, which delivered it by gravity to concave round frames, Wilfley tables and Borlase buddles, with the coarser residues being pumped separately for future treatment if necessary. The whole was driven by two steam-engines, one of which drove a 69 amp. 220 volt dynamo. Later in 1913 Edward Gamman was appointed assayer, and a Mr Vine, possibly Edward Vine of Camborne, former manager of the Bracket Tin Stream at Brea, was called in to assist the manager.

The team brought the plant into production just before the outbreak of the first World War. The plant was closed down within about twelve months of starting. In October 1919 practically the whole of the company's capital was offered for sale by the Merton company, then in liquidation, and in August 1920 the machinery and materials were put up for sale. Prospecting at the Loe Pool in 1929 did not lead to any working, but concrete tanks, foundations, walls, and a buddle built by the Helston Valley company, now much overgrown, can still be seen on the hillside above the road to Lower Nanceloe, a short distance south of the sewage-works.[145]

A little higher up the river a single stream-works at Lowertown continued to treat the wastes poured into the river by the Wendron mines until the last of them, Porkellis Tin Mine, formerly Basset and Grylls, closed about 1938 or 1939.

Buddles on the old dressing-floors of Basset and Grylls mine, Porkellis Moor. *Justin Brooke*

The Lowertown works were acquired at about this time by J. P. A. Harvey, of Lowertown, a director of South Crofty mine, Pool, whence further supplies of tin-bearing waste were obtained for dressing and subsequent sale to an agent in Penryn. The works finally closed after the 1939-45 War.[146] This was the end of tin-streaming in Wendron, though not in Cornwall. In 1954 there were still eighteen streams at work in the county,[147] and at the time of writing there are still two. The Brea Tin Stream at Camborne is owned by Medway Tin Ltd., who built a modern plant on the site of a primitive mill built after the War by the late Stephen ('Stee') Mounce, largely from materials salvaged from rubbish-dumps. The plant is now on a care and maintenance basis. The second stream is the plant at Tolgus, on the river below Redruth. After many vicissitudes it has become the 'Tolgus Charity Tin Trail', and the proceeds from its collection box go to support the Cornwall Air Ambulance. The company now running it is the successor to a concern started or acquired by the Uren family in the eighteen-seventies, from whom it passed to the Stewart family early in the present century. For some years after the death of the last of the Stewarts Tolgus was run as a tourist attraction and preserved for the benefit of visitors much tin-dressing equipment that is old-fashioned or obsolete including the only surviving working set of Cornish stamps. A third stream-work was built at Tuckingmill by Cornwall Tin and Engineering Ltd. at the end of 1979, on the site formerly occupied by the Tolgarrick Tin Stream Company in the second half of the last century, but this was closed and dismantled in 1986 following the failure of the International Tin Council to honour its bargains the previous October.

On Porkellis Moor various companies have carried out prospecting work in recent years, the most detailed study being by Consolidated Gold Fields Ltd., the London-based mining finance house with international interests (which in August 1989 was taken over by the Hanson Group). A long report on the area was prepared in 1978 by Dr M. S. Johnson and Dr R. J. Halliday, of the Department of Botany at the University of Liverpool, but after considerable work on the area the company finally decided not to go ahead with any extractive operations. In 1980-81 Gopeng Berhad, a tin-dredging company originally floated in Redruth, whose main business is in Malaya, conducted some exploratory borings. These indicated a marginal operation with tin mineralisation posing difficult separation problems, and in October 1981 the company announced that it had decided not to go ahead with developing its surface tin mining prospect. Since then no further work has been done.[148]

CHAPTER TEN
CONCLUSION

A QUESTION THAT is often asked is whether the Wendron district will ever see streaming or mining again. To this one can only reply (to use a Victorian phrase) that there must be the elements of success. Before a dredging or mining company can start work it has to complete a number of preliminary steps, not the least of which is raising the money needed. Having obtained a license or lease from the owner of the minerals, it must then get planning permission to prospect, and to do this it will have to be prepared to explain its intentions in detail at site meetings and planning inquiries. Then, having obtained permission and completed its prospecting, the company must evaluate its findings and satisfy itself that there are sufficient deposits of mineral to make it worth while working. It can then apply for planning permission to work the mineral, and this may not be granted before there has been another round of public inquiries and site meetings.

In Cornwall applications for planning permission to prospect or mine are dealt with at County level. Such permissions as are granted are subject to strict and enforceable conditions covering the restoration of the surface when the working is completed, either to its previous state or converted to some other use, such as agriculture or leisure activities. The county is fortunate in that among its residents there are experts and well-informed people willing to offer advice and to make suggestions to those affected by proposals to work minerals, so that no-one attending a planning inquiry need lack the information on which to present a case. With this expertise in matters of mining and conservation it is a cause for some satisfaction that, under the guidance of the Cornish Chamber of Mines, mining companies have for a long time been very conscious of their obligations as conservationists. It can thus be expected that if streaming or dredging is to take place on Porkellis Moor, or elsewhere, it will be subject to very stringent regulation, and, as the work proceeds, conditional upon maintaining a satisfactory balance between short-term mining requirements and the long-term needs of the landowners and residents of the district, as well as those of interested parties from further afield. The local water authorities also have considerable powers affecting mineral workings of all kinds; and here it should be noted that there is no recorded production of arsenic for the parish of Wendron.

In an area like Porkellis Moor, most of which is likely to have been worked over a number of times, the chances of finding rich deposits of stream-tin are not very great, and the profitable working of what remains might depend on the operating company's ability to sell gravel in addition to black tin. It seems unlikely that any company would wish to work the whole of the Moor at once, since much of it might be found to be unpayable.

As regards underground mining, the position is fairly clear. There has been none in the area for over fifty years, and the last dividend paid by a public company working a Wendron mine went to the adventurers in East Wheal Lovell in 1874. With the exception of the Trumpet Consols group the Wendron mines have all been on a small scale, and as their lodes have in many places been found to become poor and unprofitable to work in depth, it would be a brave company indeed that would wish to start deep mining on deposits likely to be of only marginal payability, particularly in view of other more promising and less sensitive areas elsewhere in the county.[149]

APPENDIX A
BOUNDS

The following are among the bounds recorded for Wendron. Where the names are Cornish the English equivalents are given in parentheses, followed by location if known. Dates are for the first record, such as pitching or cutting, renewal, share sale, map, or law-suit. No distinction is made between mine and stream bounds where one place was bounded for both. Unnamed bounds were cut on Boderluggan, Boscadjack, Carnebone, Laity, Manhay, Manhay Vean, Menerlue, Polhigey, Tregonebris, Tregoose, Treloar, Treloquithack, Trussall, and White Alice.

1754	Aunte Kittys Little Ball in the Feehold, White Alice
1766	Bal Dees (men's work), Porkellis Moor
1676	Ball Mean Heere (long stone workings), Halabezack
1742	Ballreeth (red workings), Lower Porkellis
1749	Beacon Lane
1754	Beggall Croft (hillock field), Halabezack
1836	Black Lion, Trenear Moor
1674	Blew Worke, Porkellis
1836	Boquio (snipe house), Porkellis Moor
1754	Bounds Bean (little bounds), White Alice
1752	Bounds Beghall (hillock bounds), Halabezack
1754	Bounds Blow (blue bounds), White Alice
1676	Bounds Calish (hard bounds)
1754	Bounds nigh Peter Dowa's Dwelling House

1656	Carledneow (holly trees), Garlidna
1827	Carn Wartha (upper outcrop), Lezerea
1676	Carnebyn, Carnebone
1507	Castle Teen Hern, Lower Town
1813	Coledna, Garlidna
1813	Colvener (hazel rock) alias Skidner Moor, Colvennor
1725	Come Sooner Next, Halwin
1676	Croft an Begall (the hillock field), Halabezack
1676	Croft Pella (further field)
1676	Dowr an Davas (the sheep's water)
1695	Fansye Bounds, Gweek
1674	Fatt Work, formerly Treseders Work
1690	Gallidniow, Garlidna
1507	Garlinny, Garlidna
1750	Glyn's Old Pair of Workings, Porkellis
1670	Goon an Castell (the fort hill), Medlyn Moor
1676	Goon Angove (the smithy hill)
1754	Goon Henver Well (old road hill work)
1749	Goonnoon (starvation hill)
1676	Goonvean (little hill)
1814	Grambla Wood (cromlech wood)
1649	Great Bounds, Manhay Vean
1801	Great Roselidden (spur lake), Roselidden
1754	Great White Allys Lane End, White Alice
1836	Greyhound, Porkellis Moor

1749	Gweek Stream, Gweek
1676	Haggarowell (ugly weather), Porkellis
1676	Halebissack (rotten moor), Halabezack
1754	Hall Harness (long moor) Moor, Garlidna
1783	Halwydden (sunshine), Halwin
1814	Hendra Moor (old house moor), Hendra
1836	Hetch an Rose (the water-wheel open-work), Porkellis Moor
1674	John Merrot's Field
1754	Lane Leading to Vellanbeeble (streams mill) Stamps, Medlyn Moor
1750	Lezerea
1695	Little Bounds, Gweek
1754	Load an Chace (hunt lode), Halabezack
1676	Load an Craft (the field lode)
1754	Loaden Hogshead (the barrel lode), Porkellis
1720	Mean Vroze (great rock), Porkellis
1676	New Engine
1838	New Leat
1754	Pack of Bounds in Beggall Croft (hillock field), Halabezack
1754	Park an Barleys (the barley field)
1751	Park an Totle (the hole field), Lower Porkellis
1754	Pellas Croft (bald oats field), Halabezack
1776	Pencoose (top wood), Lower Pencoose
1836	Penfield, Porkellis Moor
1676	Penvorth (top road)
1676	Polhigie (ducks' pool), Polmarth
1676	Polmarth (horse-pond), Polmarth
1814	Porkellis Moor
1725	Samuel Dunstone's Work, Porkellis
1676	Scorva (or Scurvey) Moor, Polmarth
1676	Stream Vean (little stream)
1793	Tregarrick and Pencoose Vean (rock farm and little top wood), Tregarrick and Tresprison
1814	Trellion

1749	Treloar and Mengearn Moor (garden farm and corn rock), Treloar
1676	Trewavas Moor (winter farm moor), Trewavas
1814	Trewavas Moor Stream, Trewavas
1515	Trewen (white farm), Trewennack
1749	Two Little Pair of Mine Bounds
1749	Tymorgy (dogfish house), Lower Porkellis
1752	Ungoose (the wood), Encoys
1801	Well Close, Roselidden
1756	Wheal Ashes, Porkellis Moor
1756	Wheal Fatt, Porkellis Moor
1749	Wheal Growan (granite gravel work), Lower Porkellis
1735	Wheal Ruby, Garlidna
1676	Wheal Vor (road work)
1676	Wheale Blow (blue work), White Alice
1507	Whele En Knappe, Kenap
1676	White Allys, White Alice
1790	White Pit, Carnkie
1498	Whyle an Pytts (the pits' work), Porkellis

APPENDIX B

TIN-STREAMERS PAYING DUES TO CAPTAIN CREASE, 1837-45, RECORDED IN BENNET JOHNS' DUES BOOK (SEE CHAPTER 7).

ANDREW, William	Rame	Retanna Mine 1839, 1841
BOLITHO, Edward	Porkellis	Halwin Moor 1837
		Garlidna Moor 1841-43
		Garlidna Stream 1845
BOLITHO, Simon	Halabezack	Polhigey Moor 1839
BOLITHO, William	Boswin	Polhigey Moor 1841
BOLITHO, William	Porkellis	Porkellis Moors 1840
CADDY, John	. . .	Wheal Hope (Trenear) 1845
CADDY, Richard.	Halabezack	Halabezack Moor 1840-41
CADDY, William	Halabezack	Halwin Moors 1845
COLLINS, Thomas	Menalue	Polmarth Moors 1842
COMBELLACK, Henry	Rame	Polhigey Moor 1840
COMBELLACK, Thomas	Carnebone	Halwin Moors 1838-39
COMBELLACK, William	Carnkie	Menalue Moor 1841
		Polhigey Moor 1840, 1842
COMBELLACK, William	Retanna	Polhigey Moor 1839
CROCKER, John	Lancarrow	Menheryon 1845
CROCKER, William	Lancarrow	Lancarrow Moor 1837-45
		Polgear Moors 1842-45
DALLY, Henry	Tremenheere	Wheal Whiddon 1840
DAVIS, Henry	Lezerea	Lezerea Moor 1843
DINNES, Thomas	Boderwennack	Roselidden Moor 1845
DUNSTAN, Thomas	Porkellis	Wheal Whiddon. 1838-39
DUNSTONE, John	Burras	Carthvean Moor 1840
GLUYAS, Henry	Trenethick	Roselidden Moor 1845

GLUYAS, Oliver	White Alice	Yellow Work Common 1839
GRIGG, John	Porkellis	Halwin Moor 1838-39, 1843
	Porkellis Moor 1839	
GRIGG, John and James	Porkellis	Halwin Moors 1840
HARRIS, James	Tremenheere	Porkellis Moor 1841
	Trenear Moor 1845	
HARRY, Ralph	Trevenen	Wheal Whiddon 1839
HODGE, William	Crahan	Treloquithack Moors 1840
JENKIN, Joseph	Carnebone	Polangrain Moor 1838
JENKIN, Joseph	Garlidna	Retanna Moors 1840
JENKIN, Joseph	Halwin	Medlyn Moors 1839
JENKIN, Joseph, William and Thomas	Halwin	Halwin Estate].840
JENKIN, William	Carnkie	Polhigey Moors 1840-41
JOHNS, William	Polmarth	Yellow Work Common 1841-44
MARTEN, George	Sithney	Wheal Dream (Trenear) 1840-41
MOYLE, Bennett	Porkellis	Lezerea Moor 1837
		Porkellis Moor 1838-40
MOYLE, Edward	Menalue	Polhigey Moor 1838-44
MOYLE, E (senior)	Porkellis	Porkellis Moors 1838
MOYLE, Edward	Boswin	Porkellis Moor 1839-40, 1842
		Trenear Moor 1839, 1842
MOYLE, Edward (junior)	Porkellis	Porkellis Moor 1837-41
MOYLE, James	Carnkie	Halabezack Moor 1839-40
MOYLE, James	Lezerea	Porkellis Moor 1837-38

MOYLE, John	Carnmenellis	Yellow Work Common 1840			Menheryon Moors 1838
MOYLE, John	Viscar	Medlyn Moor 1837	PRYOR, John	Lowertown	Wheal Trumpet 1841-44
		Polhigey Moor 1840-41	PRYOR, John	Menheryon	Polhigey Moor 1842-43
MOYLE, John	Halabezack	Polmarth Moors 1842	PRYOR, Richard	Halwin	Halwin 1842
MOYLE, John	Halwin	Halwin Moor 1838			Halwin Moor 1843
MOYLE, Peter	Carthvean	Carthvean. Moor 1838-39	PRYOR, Sampson	Menheryon	Yellow Work Moor 1845
MOYLE, Peter	Hendra	Porkellis Moor 1837-40	PRYOR, Thomas		
MOYLE, Richard	Carnkie	Polhigey Moor 1837-39	and Richard	Halwin	Halwin Moor 1845
MOYLE, Stephen	Lezerea	Lezerea Moor 1841-42, 1844	PRYOR, William	Trenear	Trenear Moor 1841
MOYLE, Stephen and John	Lezerea	Porkellis Moor 1839-43	REED, Richard	Halwin	Halwin Moors 1840
MOYLE, Thomas	Carnkie	Polhigey Moor 1837,	RICHARDS, John	Porkellis	Porkellis Moors 1843
		Polhigey Moor 1841	RICHARDS, Thomas	Viscar	Halwin Moors 1840
MOYLE, Thomas			ROBARTS, John	Garlidna	Halwin Moors 1840-41
and Richard	Carnkie	Polhigey Moor 1840-43	ROBARTS, John	Halabezack	Menalue Moor 1838
		Croft Pellow (Halwin) 1841-45			Polhigey Moors 1842-44
MOYLE, William	Viscar	Medlyn Moor 1838-42	ROBARTS, William	Halabezack	Halabezack Stennacks 1844
		Polhigey Moor 1838-39	SPARGO, William	Carnkie	Polhigey Moor 1837-40, 1845
MOYLE, William	Garlidna	Medlyn Moor 1841, 1844	THOMAS, Tobias	Bodilly	Bodilly 1842
MOYLE, William	Porkellis	Lezerea Moor 1837, 1839-43	TOY, William	Grigangrows	Lancarrow Moors 1837
PASCOE, Thomas	Halwin	Halwin Moors 1839-41	TRELOAR Benjamin	Stithians	Halwin Moor 1839
PASCOE, Walter	Halwin	Halwin Stream 1843	TRELOAR, Daniel	Halwin	Halwin Moor 1843
PASCOE, William	Porkellis	Halwin Moors 1838-39	TRESIDDER, John	Menalue	Yellow Work Moor 1843
PEARCE, William	Halwin	Medlyn Moor 1842	TRESIDDER, Thomas	Carnkie	Polhigey Moor 1838
PENALUNA, Alex	Retanna	Retanna Moor 1838			Medlyn Moors 1839-40
PENALUNA, John	Trenear	Trenear Moors 1840-45			Balmynheer 1845
PENALUNA, Zacharias	Trenear	Trenear Moor 1837-39	TRESIDDER, Thomas	Viscar	Medlyn Moor 1843
PERRY, Peter	Viscar	Menadue Moor 1837	TRESIDDER, Thomas	Medlyn	Medlyn Moors 1841-42
		Menalue Moor 1838	TRESIDDER, Walter	Medlyn	Medlyn Moor 1841-42
		Polhigey Moor 1838-39	TRESIDDER, William	Carnkie	Menheryon Moor 1841
		Medlyn Moors 1838-44			Polhigey Moor 1843, 1845
		Polhigey Moors 1845	WEARN, Daniel	Carnebone	Crowgey and
PERRY, Richard	. . .	Wheal Trumpet 1839			Treloar Moors 1841
PERRY, William	Viscar	Medlyn Moors 1838, 1842	WEARN, James	Laity	Treloar Moor 1841
PRISK, Joseph	Carnmenellis	Balmynheer 1844	WEARN, John	Lezerea	Lezerea or
PRISK, Samuel	Caladnack	Porkellis Moor 1839			Porkellis Moors 1843
PRYOR, John	Carthew	Lancarrow Moor 1837	WILLIAMS, Walter	Halabezack	Halabezack 1841

APPENDIX C
GLOSSARY OF STREAMING AND MINING TERMS

Back | The top or outcrop of a lode.

Bal | Tin-stream, openwork or mine. 'A place of digging' (1754); 'a parcel of tin-works' (1790); now a term of affection for a working mine.

Ball | A group or cluster of stream works or mines.

Bargain-buyer | One who buys small quantities of ore for further dressing and sale.

Bill, Smelter's | Also tin-bill. A smelter's promissory note, acknowleging the receipt of a stated quantityof black tin and undertaking to deliver a specific quantity of tin metal at the next coinage. After the abolition of coinage in 1837 the term was applied to a smelter's receipt for black tin, and showed the purchase consideration.

Black tin | Tin ore dressed ready for the smelter, containing up to 70% metal.

Blowing-house | Primitive smelting-works, using a draught from a bellows.

Burning-house | Plant in which partly-dressed tin ore is roasted to remove sulphur and arsenic.

Burrow | Heap of waste mine rock or spoil.

Casualties | Waste from early tin-dressing operations; now called slimes.

Conventionary rent | A nominal rent payable by tenants of land in the Duchy manors when they were held under perpetually renewable leases.

Cost-book company | A mining partnership in transferable shares.

Deads | Waste rock containing no mineral.

Dressing | The operations involved in separating black tin or other mineral from worthless waste.

Goosework | Wrought iron stays with flattened and broadened ends supporting launders, and bearing a fanciful resemblance to a goose with outstretched neck.

Growan | Granite pebbles, gravel or grit.

Halvans | Low-grade partly-dressed ore.

Headwear | A device to stop water flowing down a leat and to divert it back to its original bed.

Hatch | Timber-lined shaft sunk through an alluvial deposit.

Hetch | Also hutch. Open-working on the back of a lode; now 'etch, a water-filled openwork.

Hownan | Wendron word for a stockworks or open working on a deposit of tin ore occurring in numerous thin veins or strings, necessitating the removal of the whole mineralised deposit.

Jew's house | Primitive smelting-works.

Kieve | Tub or barrel.

Killas	Slate; the general term in Cornwall for sedimentary rocks, from the Cornish carrick laze, blue (or green) rock.
Mineral lord	Owner of the minerals under a piece of ground, not necessarily the owner of the surface.
Moor(s)	Extensive barren waste, sometimes marshy.
Old men	Stream or mine workers in past centuries.
Openwork	Excavation on the back of a lode; see hatch, hownan, stennack.
Pare	Also pair; a gang of any number of men.
Pednan	Head of a buddle (Cornish pen, head).
Pitch	A particular length, breadth (and sometimes depth) of ground set to tributers.
Purser	Secretary of a cost-book company.
Rag-and-chain pump	An endless chain with knobs of cord, stiffened with leather, at intervals, which passed over a hand-turned sprocket-wheel, down into the openwork or mine and up through a wooden pipe, through which it drew water. Forerunner of the Bastier pump.
Returning charges	The cost of dressing, preparing, and carrying black tin to the smelter.
Sample, to	To assay and weigh black tin prior to sale.
Set and let	The right to set pitches in or to sub-let the whole of a leased or bounded area.
Sett	Area of ground leased for mining; the lease itself.
Shelf	Bedrock beneath an alluvial deposit.
Slimes	Very fine waste left from dressing tin ore., containing tin residues; see casualties.
Sollar	Platform over or in a shaft.
Sordes	Dregs or leavings from tin dressing.
Stannary	An administrative area for tin-mining; a medieval tin-working.
Stennack	Tin-ground; tin-workings. Occurs in names of openworks and fields.
Tin-streamer	Worker in an alluvial deposit or on waste from stamping-mills.
Toller	Collector of dues or royalties for the mineral lord.
Tributer	Streamer or miner who works for an agreed proportion of the value of the ore he recovers from waste or tailings, or sends to surface.
Wheal	Cornish for work, hence a mine-working. Gwel, a field, is sometimes corrupted to wheal.
Whits	Calcined tin ore.
Whole ground	Ground not previously worked for mineral.

REFERENCES

The title and date of works quoted are given in the Bibliography. References below give the surname of the author and date of publication. Names of publishers of recent works are given in parentheses. The following abbreviations are used:

C.R.O.	County Record Office, Truro
D.C.R.S.	Devon & Cornwall Record Society
D.C.O.	Duchy of Cornwall Office, London
I.M.M	Institution of Mining and Metallurgy
Kelly	Kelly's Directory of Cornwall
MJ	Mining Journal
MR	Mining Review
MW	Mining World
Min. Stats.	Official Mineral Statistics
P.R.O.	Public Record Office, Kew
RCG	Royal Cornwall Gazette
R.G.S.C	Royal Geological Society of Cornwall, Penzance
R.I.C.	Royal Institution of Cornwall, Truro
WB	West Briton
1840 Map	Tithe Apportionment Map, 1840
1880 Map	Ordnance Survey 25-in. Map, 1880

1. Norden c.1584, p.11.
2. Carew 1723 pp.8, 11.
3. Dines 1956 p.245
4. Borlase 1758 pp.160-61 and plate xvii. Heaps of waste rock on mines in Cornwall are also called deads.
5. Henwood 1873 p.13.
6. 1840 Map, No. 2238, $3\frac{1}{2}$ acres, furze.
7. Henwood 1873 p.200.
8. Hunt 1884 p.411.
9. Collins 1912 p.380
10. Pryce 1778 p.135.
11. Hatcher 1973 p.46; Pryce 1778 p.132.
12. Carew 1723 p.50 f.
13. Collins 1912 p.383.
14. Hatcher 1973 p.46.
15. Carew 1723 p.19.
16. Henwood 1843 p.129.
17. At Grid Ref. SW 690 320
18. Norden c1584 p.52.
19. Concanen 1830, Appendix p.176; Quentrall 1865.
20. Bennet Johns' Dues Book, 1837-45 (in private possession).
21. Tehidy Memorandum Book, R.I.C.
22. MJ 4 September 1858. The 'Phoenician' tradition, which became popular in the eighteenth century, is still current, despite the lack of convincing evidence. See note 123; Taylor 1932 p.6; Hatcher 1973 pp.2, 9. Traces of a pre-1880 clay-works can be seen at Grid Ref. SW 691 319.
23. S. J. Wills, in *Western Daily Mercury*, 13 July 1875.

24. Hunt 1884 pp.411-12.

25. Pryce 1778 p.134.

26. Henwood 1843 p.55.

27. Hunt 1884 p.412. Similar cavities formed during the ice age have been found in granite outcrops in the south of Finland, where they are known as devils' churns (*hiidenkirnut*).

28. 23 Hen.8 c.8 (1531-32); Laws of the Stannaries (1754), p.113. The rag-and-chain pump went out of general use in the second half of the eighteenth century; see R. N. Worth in MW 5 July 1873.

29. Cunnack 1867 p.52. A similar stone is preserved at Trenethick Barton.

30. MJ 27 July 1889. In the west Cornwall dialect accented 'a' becomes 'o'.

31. Carew 1723 edition p.12; Borlase 1758 pp. 177-80 and plate xix; Pryce 1778 pp.133-35 and plate v.

32. Pryce 1778 pp.135-36.

33. Carew 1723 edition p.16; 1811 edition p.50 f.; Pryce 1778 p.137: Penaluna 1819 p.253; J. Hawkins 1832 p.72; Anon. 1835 pp.182, 190, 193; Leifchild 1855 p.209; Spargo 1872 p.11.

34. Henwood 1832 p.145; Henwood 1873 pp.3, 12-13, 61.

35. MJ 23 April, 16 July, 30 July 1836, 11 August 1857; RCG 22 July, 29 July 1837, 23 March 1838.

36. The Cunnack Manuscript, (ed.) Justin Brooke, 1993, p.29.

37. S. J. Wills, MS. c1890, R.I.C.

38. RCG 8 August 1812, R. L. Clowes, D.C.O., letter 14 December 1928, per the late Dr A. K. Hamilton Jenkin. In Cornish a single 'f' is sometimes sounded as a 'v'; see Nance 1955.

39. Pounds 1982 pp.45-49. The knocking-mills listed here were probably an early form of stamping-mill. See Map by Wm. Alexander, Br.Lib. Add. MS.69461.

40. Tithe Apportionment, 1840; DD.EN.510, 520, 528/1, 531/1-2; DD.GR.406, C.R.O.

41. DD.EN.509, 510, 520, 528/1-3, 530, 1568. In 1710 Mr Enys had the right of Porkellis Wartha (Upper Porkellis) water and Mr Glyn that of Porkellis Woolas (Lower Porkellis).

42. S. J. Wills, MS. c1890, R.I.C.; DD. GR.400, C.R.O.

43. Henderson Calendar 5, p.260, No.1848, R.I.C.

44. DD.GR.411, C.R.O.

45. AD.216/1/9, C.R.O. The use of the words 'adit' and 'tail' to mean 'leat' and 'head' is unusual.

46. Wallis 23 April 1781, 15 October 1796; 1840 Map; Cost-book, R.I.C.; Lemon Map, C.R.O.

47. Official List of Mines, 1893 p.217; Lemon Map, C.R.O.; information per Clive Carter.

48. RCG 4 March 1809; 1880 Map. These may have been one of the two sets of stamps referred to as Captain Roberts's works and Captain Williams's works. A third unnamed stamping-mill was also at work lower down the river at this time; see RCG 17 February 1882.

49. DD.GR.412, C.R.O.

50. De la Beche 1839 p.583; Cost-books, R.I.C.

51. Wallis 13 September 1794, 9 November 1813, 14 August 1814; DD.TLP.545/1, C.R.O.

52. Tehidy Memorandum Book, R.I.C.

53. Penaluna 1819 p.237.

54. DD.CF.2321, C.R.O.

55. Wallis 16 September 1781, 30 July, 8 August, 1 October 1796; WB 3 November 1811; RCG 29 September 1821, 23 February 1822.

56. 1840 Map; MJ 10 April 1858; Official List of Mines, 1893 p.217; Wallis 19 June 1811.

57. Pryce 1778 p.293; Pennington 1963 pp.137-46.

58. S. J. Wills, MS. c1890, R.I.C.; Henwood 1873 pp.61-65.

59. Le Grice 1841 pp.41-45.

60. Warrants and Patents, 1729-43, per the late Dr A. K. Hamilton Jenkin; Pryce 1778 pp.136-37; Consolidated Tin Smelters Ltd. Annual Report, 31 May 1959.

61. R. L. Clowes, D.C.O., letter c.1930, quoting Caption of

Seisin, Duchy Manor of Helston in Kerrier, per the late Dr A. K. Hamilton Jenkin.

62. Concanen 1830 Appendix p.119.

63. Polsue 1872/1974 Vol. IV p.75 Appendix; Henderson Calendar 7, p.187, R.I.C.

64. Pounds 1982 pp.47-49; Cunnack 1867 p.53; Henderson 1937 p.228.

65. RCG 3 December 1803; DD.X.78/11/1-4, C.R.O.

66. DD.BL.77-24, C.R.O.

67. MJ 23 June 1849 (Smirke); 13 November 1880.

68. Laws of the Stannaries (1754) p.61; Bainbridge 1841 pp.470-71; Smirke 1843 p.73; Pennington 1963 p.145.

69. Deed in private possession.

70. X.78/11/1-4, C.R.O.: Moody 1782; 1784 (Senior 73/C, P.R.O.); Professor Robert R. Pennington, letter 25 January 1982.

71. Pennington 1963 p.78; Laws of the Stannaries (1754), p.60.

72. Laws of the Stannaries (1754), pp.42, 60, 101; Collier 1855 p.19.

73. E.g. DD.EN.1573, C.R.O.

74. Smirke 1843 Appendix p.61.

75. Carew 1723 p.10.

76. J. P. Basset's Bounds Book, 1754 (in private possession).

77. Smirke 1843 Appendix p.67.

78. Per C. P. Hill Esq., C.B., C.B.E. The earliest reference to a fraction of a tin working seen by the writer is from Alternun, in a deed dated 23 November 1439.

79. WB 3 May 1811; RCG 28 January, 29 May 1815. Cornwall's first Mining Exchange was opened in Camborne at the end of 1862; see MJ 15 November 1862.

80. MJ 23 April, 30 April 1836. Frederick Hill, of Grylls & Hill, was the author of a paper on the origin and nature of bounds; see MR 1840 pp.9, 18, 28.

81. MJ 21 May, 16 July, 30 July 1836; WB 15 July 1836.

82. Laws of the Stannaries (1754) p.61; Bassett 1839 pp.14-23.

83. Smirke 1843 pp.37-44.

84. Collier 1855 pp.18-21, 31-35; MJ 25 January 1845, 28 August 1847; Pennington 1963 pp.98-100. It is understandable that 'bounder' came to mean a person who takes an unfair advantage of another.

85. MJ 7 July, 21 July 1855, 27 February 1858; Stannary Court Records, C.R.O. For a description of the various types of company in the mining industry see Brooke 1980 p.17.

86. Crease v Sawle (in error), 2 Q.B. 862 (1842); Collier 1855 p.59; MR 30 April 1840.

87. De la Beche 1839 p.583; MJ 12 May 1866. See also R. N. Worth in MW 7 June, 5 July, 12 July 1873.

88. Deed formerly in the Tehidy Minerals Ltd. collection, now lost. A full transcript is given in Buckley 1987 p.63. The Hagarowell adit is probably the one referred to by Dines 1956 p.249, as the Halwin adit.

89. Norden 1727 p.52; Jos. Reed jr: Map of Porkellis Moor, c1836, Mining Record Office serial 47.

90. Henderson Calendar 5, p.260, No. 847, R.I.C.

91. Carew 1723 edition p.10; DD.EM.509, C.R.O.

92. DD.EN.1573, C.R.O.

93. Tehidy Abstracts Book, 1751 (in private possession). The property later became part of Porkellis United Mines and then of Basset and Grylls Mine.

94. Hitchins and Drew 1824, Vol.II, p.67.

95. Pryce 1778 p.132: Henwood 1873 p.61. In the eighteenth and nineteenth centuries stream and mine leases often specified the minimum number of men to be employed.

96. Information per Keith Skues Esq.; Crease v Barret, L Cr M. & R. 919 (1835).

97. RCG 3 October 1812, 24 April, 8 May 1813, 30 April, 7 May 1814, 7 February 1818; WB 27 August 1813, 29 April 1814, 11 June 1819.

98. WB 20 October 1815; RCG 28 October 1815, 25 September 1830. There were 39 Duchy manors containing tin mines.

99. James 1837 Vol.I, pp.49-50 f.; Vol.VI p.316; O'Byrne 1849 p.240.

100. Parcel 1 Q.3, D.C.O.; Concanen 1830 pp.207-08; Collier 1855 p.59; RCG 28 August, 30 October, 4 December 1830.

101. Information from the late Stanley Opie Esq., D.C.O.; RCG 14 July 1830.

102. RCG 21 July, 1 December 1832, 11 January 1834; Parcel 1 Q.3, D.C.O. The bulk of the £9,800-odd represented copper dues, farmed earlier in the century to Sir William Lemon; tin dues for the seven years to 1836 averaged only £787 annually.

103. MJ 11 December 1852, 1 January 1853; Kelly (Devon) 1856 p.224; Navy Lists 1862-63.

104. RCG 23 May 1835; MJ 29 August 1835, 7 November 1846; I Jurist 840 Ex. Eq. (reported 1837).

105. Crease v Barrett, note 96; RCG 13 December 1834; MJ 29 August 1835, 7 May 1836.

106. RCG 11 May 1833, 12 August 1836; Kelly 1873 p.892; 1893 p.1317; 1906 p.362; 1919 p.359; D.C.O. letter 7 March 1980.

107. Nance 1948 p.7.

108. Yellow Wort only grows on calcareous soils; the soil of Wendron is acid (per Miss Rosaline Murphy). Wendron is singular in having tin-working areas distinguished by the three primary colours.

109. Sabine 1966 p.61.

110. Hill 1906 p.312; Geevor Tin Mines plc: Annual Report 16 June 1986 (from which black tin sales estimated).

111. Dines 1956 p.261. For the subsequent history of this mine see Brooke 1980 pp.24, 31.

112. MJ 4 June 1842 (reported in error as Hartley v Gilbert); Lake 1872 p.312.

113. Penaluna 1819 p.253; J. T. Rapson, letters 1924, per the late Dr A. K. Hamilton Jenkin. See also Jenkin 1927 p.62 (a classic work). Mamelukes or Mamalukes (from the Arabic for slave) were originally Turkish and Circassian slaves in Egypt, who became a formidable military force. The last of them were slain by Mehemet Ali in Cairo in 1811.

114. Per the late Frank Richards, Porkellis.

115. MJ 27 September 1862, 4 January 1913; Williams 1862 pp.27-31. The location of the sixth engine is not known.

116. Henwood 1832 p.156 f.

117. Books in private possession.

118. Pryce 1778 p.227.

119. Ferguson 1873 p.139 and Plate 49; Graham 1954 p.3. See also illustrations in Hill 1906.

120. MJ 28 August, 4 September 1858. See also DD.X.106/24, 25, C.R.O.

121. Per the late Frank Richards, Porkellis. The approximate site of the subsidence, since filled in, is Grid Ref: SW 688 323.

122. MJ 4 September 1858, 4 August 1860. For details of the disaster which claimed 38 lives see Douch 1964, pp.42-48.

123. E.g. Borlase 1754 pp. 25-32, quoting Pliny, Strabo and others; Carew 1723 p.8. See note 22.

124. Haydn 1873 pp.378, 514; Encyclopaedia Britannica 1929 Vol.13 p.57.

125. MJ 26 September 1857, 9 January, 4 September 1858; Brooke, J. (ed.) The Cunnack Manuscript, 1993 p.31.

126. DD.EN.1573, C.R.O.; Lady Basset's Dues Account, Wendron, Tehidy Collection, C.R.O.; Cunnack 1867; Jenkin 1977 p.23. In 1847-51 Henry Jenkin sold 5 tons 9¾ cwts. of black tin for £307.6s.9d., from Wheal an Grease.

127. MJ 26 October 1872, 27 September 1873, 1 August 1874; MW 11 January, 13 September, 27 September, 8 November 1873; RCG 12 October 1877. Earlier writers, giving higher figures for the number of stream-works, have included those on the river running from Wheal Basset to Portreath.

128. Min. Stats. 1859-83; S. J. Wills in *Western Daily Mercury*, 29 July 1875; F. J. Stephens, 1887 p.126 (in Rep.

Royal Cornwall Polytechnic Society); 8 February 1913 (in Tin & Copper World); Official List of Mines, 1883 p.217.

129. MJ 28 February, 27 June 1891, 9 April, 14 May 1892.

130. Per D.C.O.

131. Per Mr L. Christophers, Helston.

132. Jenkin 1927 pp.21, 23; DD.EN.1782, C.R.O.

133. Prospectus per Messrs. Reginald Rogers & Son, Helston; Hunt 1884 p.355; Jenkin 1962 p.54.

134. Per the late Dr A. K. Hamilton Jenkin, quoting the late T. S. Bolitho.

135. Henwood 1873 p.201; note 16, p.55; Hunt 1884 p.413; Symons 1884 p.169.

136. MJ 8 June 1850, 29 March 1851, 21 February, 28 February 1852, 22 January 1853, 22 September 1855, 5 December 1857, 9 January 1858, 13 October 1860, 30 August 1862, 30 September 1865; Min. Stats. 1858-60; J. J. Rogers 1865 p.352 (in Trans. R.G.S.C.); R. S. Bryant: Report Book, 16 June 1860, C.R.O.

137. MW 16 March 1872.

138. Henwood 1873 p.60.

139. RCG 24 August 1877.

140. Min. Stats. 1877-81.

141. RCG 17 February 1882.

142. Min. Stats. 1870-78.

143. Official List of Mines, 1893 p.217.

144. MW 15 June 1912. The Banka Drill was first demonstrated in Cornwall in 1910; see MJ 11 June 1910.

145. MJ 1 February, 10 May 1913, 25 October 1919, 17 July 1920, 5 October 1929, 25 January 1930; Trans. Cornish Institute of Engineers, 1913 p.108; Trans. I.M.M. 1919 p.326; Stock Exchange Register of Defunct and other Companies, 1955 p.298.

146. Jenkin 1980 p.56. The 1880 Map shows Treworlis Works on the south bank above the bridge at Lowertown.

147. Graham 1954 p.2.

148. Ecological and Conservation Value Assessments and their Integration with Proposed Alluvial Tin Mine, Porkellis Moor, near Helston, 1978 (Consolidated Gold Fields Ltd.); MJ 9 October 1981.

149. E.g. in W. E. Sevier and others, 1979 pp.B33-40 (in Trans. I.M.M. vol. 88).

BIBLIOGRAPHY

Anon. *Minerals & Metals, &c,* S.P.C.K. 1835

Bainbridge on Mines, 1841

Bassett, J. *Origin and History of the Bounding Custom,* 1839
de la Beche, (Sir) Henry. *Report on the Geology of Cornwall, &c.,* 1839

Borlase, William. *Antiquities Of Cornwall,* 1754

Borlase, William. *The Natural History of Cornwall,* 1758

Brooke, Justin. *Stannary Tales,* Twelveheads Press 1980

Brooke, Justin (ed.) The Cunnack Manuscript, *Trevithick Society,* 1993.

Buckley, J. A. *Tudor Tin Bounds, West Penwith,* Dyllansow Truran 1987

Carew, Richard. MS. c.1586, printed as *The Survey of Cornwall,* 1602 (1723 edition).

Collier, R. P. *A Treatise on the Law relating to Mines,* 2nd edition, 1855

Collins, J. H. Observations on the West of England Mining Region, *Trans R.G.S.C.* 1912

Concanen, George, *A Report of the Trial at Bar, Rowe v Brenton,* 1830

Ecological and Conservation Value Assessments and their Integration with Proposed Alluvial Tin Mine, Porkellis Moor, near Helston, Consolidated Gold Fields Ltd. 1978

Cunnack, R. J. *Proc. Miners' Association of Cornwall and Devonshire* 1867

Dines, H. G. *The Metalliferous Mining Region of South-West England,* H.M.S.O. 1956

Douch, H. L. *East Wheal Rose,* D. Bradford Barton Ltd. 1964. *Duchy of Cornwall, 1649-51,* Devon & Cornwall Record Society 1982

Encyclopaedia Britannica 1929

Ferguson, Henry T. *Proc. Institute of Mechanical Engineers* 1873

Graham, R. J. *Camborne School of Mines Magazine* 1954

Hatcher, John. *English Tin Production and Trade before 1550,* Oxford University Press 1973

Hawkins, J. *Trans. R.G.S.C.* 1832

Haydn's Dictionary of Dates, 1873

Henderson, Charles. *History of the Parish of Constantine,* R.I.C. 1937

Henwood, William Jory. *Trans. R.G.S.C.* 1832

Henwood, William Jory. The Metalliferous Deposits of Cornwall and Devon, *Trans. R.G.S.C.* 1843

Henwood, William Jory. in *Journal R.I.C.* reprint 1873

Hill, J. B. and others *The Geology Of Falmouth and Truro, &c.,* H.M.S.O. 1906

Hitchins and Drew *History of Cornwall, Vol.II* 1824,

Hunt, Robert, *British Mining,* 1884

James, William. *Naval History of Great Britain, Vol.I; Vol.VI* 1837

Jenkin, A. K. Hamilton, *The Cornish Miner,* George Allen & Unwin Ltd. 1927

Jenkin, A. K. Hamilton, *Mines and Miners of Cornwall, part iv* Truro Bookshop 1962

Jenkin, A. K. Hamilton, *Wendron Tin,* Wendron Forge Ltd. 1977

Lake's Parochial History of Cornwall, vol.iv 1872

Le Grice, Rev. C. V. *Trans. R.G.S.C.* 1841

Leifchild, J. R. *Cornwall, Its Mines and Miners,* 1855

Moody, Charles. *A Survey of Tin Bounds &c.* R.I.C. 1782

Nance, R. Morton p.7 *Old Cornwall, vol. iv* 1948

Nance, R. Morton. *Cornish-English Dictionary,* Federation of Old Cornwall Societies 1955

Norden, John, MS. c.1584, subsequently revised and edited, and printed as *Speculi Britanniae Pars,* 1727

O'Byrne's Naval Dictionary, 1849

Penaluna, William *The Circle,* 1819

Pennington, Robert R. *Stannary Law,* David & Charles 1963

Pounds, Professor Norman J. G. (ed.) *Parliamentary Survey of the Duchy of Cornwall, 1649–51,* 1982, D.C.R.S.

Pryce, William *Mineralogia Cornubiensis,* 1778

Quentrall, Thomas. *Map of Wendron Mining District,* No. 72. Mining Record Office 1865

Sabine, B. E. V. *A History of Income Tax,* George Allen & Unwin Ltd. 1966

Smirke, Edward *The Case of Vice against Thomas,* 1843

Spargo, Thomas. *The Tin Mines of Cornwall and Devon,* 1872

Laws of the Stannaries, (1753)

Stock Exchange Register of Defunct and other Companies, 1955

Symons, Brenton. *The Geology of Cornwall,* 1884

Taylor, Canon T. *St Michael's Mount,* Oxford University Press 1932

Christopher Wallis' Journal, R.I.C.

Williams, J. *Cornwall and Devon Mining Directory,* 1862

MAP REFERENCES

TIN-STREAMS, STAMPS AND MINES

The following references are approximate; doubtful or inferred locations are given in parentheses, and the list is not exhaustive.

Ann, Wheal	678 303	Helston Valley Stream Works	651 268
Balcoath and Wheal Jane	696 340	Lancarrow Moor	691 374
Balmynheer	700 345	Lezerea Higher Stamps	(688 339)
Ball Reeth Adit	691 326	Lezerea Lower Stamps	(689 339)
Basset and Grylls Mine	692 330	Lezerea Moor	688 340
Bodilly Stamps	676 313	Loe Pool	650 251
Boswin Mine	(694 339)	Lovell, Wheal	693 305
Carn Wartha	687 355	Lowertown Stamps (Treworlis)	659 291
Castle Wary Works	653 267	Mean Vrose	(689 332)
Caudle, Wheal	(652 260)	Medlyn Mines	708 334
Chenhall	(678 316)	Medlyn Moor	706 337
Coldwind Stamps	684 343	Mellen Beblo	705 330
Colvennor Moor	712 363	Menadue Moor	722 360
Coverack Stamps	670 30	Menerlue Moor	715 355
Crosshole Stamps	(687 339	Menheryon Moor	702 372
Foster, Wheal	694 327	Polangrain	708 324
Friendship, Wheal	(688 328)	Polgear Moor	658 368
Garlidna	698 328	Polhigey Moor	713 352
Gwealhellis Stream	(657 289)	Pool Wheal	653 263
Glebe Stamps	677 312	Porkellis Moor	688 324
Hagarowell Stamps	(699 331)	Retanna	709 323
Halwin Stream	699 333	Roselidden (Roseline)	672 297
Helston Stream Works	654 272	Ruby, Wheal	700 329
		Salena Stamps	679 313
		Sithney Coverack Stamps	668 301

Tolgus Tin	690 442
Treloar and Crowgey	698 303
Trelubbas Stamps	666 298
Trenear	682 314
Trenithick Wood Mine	672 295
Trewavas Downs	692 322
Trumpet Consols	674 302
Tymorgy, Wheal	693 329
Weeth Green	652 268
Wendron Consols	687 318
White Alice Stamps	692 349
Wood Stamps	692 292
Yellow Work Common	706 365
Yellow Work Moor	708 364

SUBJECT INDEX

INDEX OF SURNAMES